THE RETI

YORK

Audry Lambert
York 1991

The front cover shows a picture of the original 18th C. Frontage of The Retreat, which still exists today.

ISBN 0 900657 88 X

Phototypeset and Printed by William Sessions Limited
The Ebor Press, York, England

THE RETREAT
YORK

An Early Quaker Experiment in the Treatment of Mental Illness

By

Mary R. Glover, MA, OXON

One time Fellow of St. Hugh's College, Oxford,
and later Director of Social Studies, Keele University

Edited
by
Janet R. Glover, CBE, MA, OXON

WILLIAM SESSIONS LIMITED
YORK, ENGLAND
1984

Contents

Illustrations

Acknowledgments and Thanks

Mary Glover was specially conscious of her indebtedness to Eric Southall, who read and re-read her scripts, offering constructive suggestions and comments; also to her doctor, Dr. E. V. Bevan, who took a continuing interest in her work, and insisted that she must go on working at it, which she did, to the end.

Her friends Professor Dorothy Emmet and Margaret Braithwaite gave her much encouragement, and were instrumental in getting three articles published in the journal of the Epiphany Philosophers, *Theoria to Theory*, some of which with their permission she has used in this book. She also wished to record her thanks to the Editor of the *Nursing Mirror*, for which Mary wrote some articles in 1964. Some of this material too has been used in this book with the Editor's agreement.

Mary greatly valued the help given her by Daphne Richards over a number of years, particularly in the taxing business of co-ordinating revised passages, and typing and re-typing, often at short notice.

The use of the Cambridge University Library was an inestimable privilege to her for reading, research and continuous checking, this she never ceased to appreciate, and expressly wished her debt to the Librarian and his most helpful staff to be recorded.

She was also most grateful to Dr. J.E. O'N. Gillespie, formerly Medical Director of The Retreat, and to his secretary, Miss Eileen Cope, and their colleagues who allowed her to spend many hours reading The Retreats' archives *in situ*. She appreciated too the interest and help given her by Dr. Clark of Fulbourn Hospital, both in discussion and correspondence.

Mary gave close attention to the work of Professor Kathleen Jones on the history of mental illness and its treatment. She often spoke of Professor Jones' generous response to various questions about which she consulted her. Edward H. Milligan, the Librarian at Friends' House, Euston Road, London, provided ready access to important background material for which Mary was grateful.

During her closing years the Rev. Peter Cameron was a regular visitor and Mary found that her conversations with him about this book, and indeed a host of other matters, greatly encouraged her. Over the years many other friends gave her stimulating practical help. These included

Joan Calland, the late Mary Cudworth, Vera Dodge, Alice Eden, Biddy Gibson, the late Lorel Goodfellow, Dr. Earle Owen, Damaris Parker-Rhodes and Sylvia Watson. There must be many others to whom she turned for advice and whose comments and interest she valued. We regret that we may not have the names of all those who helped her in various ways, but whom she would wish to thank.

Authors are always heartened when their publishers prove sympathetic and perceptive. On Mary's behalf we offer our warm gratitude to William and Margaret Sessions who have given this book such personal interest and care.

Cambridge
March 1984.

Janet R. Glover
and
Elizabeth R. Glover

Mary R. Glover

Prologue

Mary Reaveley Glover, 1898—1982

Mary was the eldest of a family of six brothers and sisters. From early childhood she began to show characteristics which friends and colleagues recognised as hallmarks throughout her life. Even as a child she became aware of misfits and people in trouble, and was quick to help them if she could. No illogicality passed her unchallenged. Always spirited, adventurous, with a keen love of the comic, she was one to experiment and richly enjoy a multitude of interests, painting, botanising, bird-watching, canoe-trips and so on. Later on she travelled widely, not only in Europe but in the Far East and Canada. She was an insatiable reader in several languages and conversation was the breath of life to her. Her gift for friendship was a lifelong feature and her circle of friends embraced people of many nationalities and all ages, from small children to the aged.

Her academic career followed the usual pattern of a future don: a scholarship to Somerville College, Oxford, and a First in Greats, followed by teaching Classics at King Edward's School, Birmingham, and Westfield College, London, and so back to Oxford as Greats Tutor at St. Hugh's College. Here her responsibilities included teaching political science to students of History and PPE. While she retained her love of Classics all her life, she had an addiction to Philosophy which never left her.

Then the war came, and broke the pattern. She volunteered for war service and this took her to the Ministry of Labour. Later she worked on the bench in the Bristol Aero Space Company and subsequently in a Midlands pottery factory. These experiences revealed the devastating, soul-destroying nature of mechanical and repetitive work, particularly on the moving belt. The mental impoverishment which affected people who were engaged in mass production appalled her, and led to her publishing *Democracy and Industry* (Chatto and Windus 1947) under the name of Constance Reaveley, in collaboration with a colleague, John Winnington. During this time she lived as a lodger in working class homes, and under war-time conditions learned at first hand some of the deprivations accepted at that time as normal for the underprivileged. She lectured in the evenings for W.E.A. classes, getting around in unfamiliar areas during the blackout with diminishing sources of fuel supply for her ancient Austin Seven.

When A.D. Lindsay appointed her to the Social Science Department as a foundation member of the new University College of North Staffordshire — later to become the University of Keele — she was therefore well equipped on several levels. Here, as at Oxford, students enjoyed her academic teaching, as one of them wrote 'subjecting themselves to that rapier mind'. Colleagues as well as students found delight in her conversation, her merry wit, her parties, her hospitality, her infectious laughter. Many have told us that they found relief and comfort in discussing personal troubles with her, of a religious as well as an intellectual or emotional nature. Her personal faith was a central factor in her life, based upon her rigorous outreach for truth, rather than upon conventional traditions. As always she was prepared to disagree on occasion and to say why. This did not terminate the conversations but widened them and cemented friendships which continued to the end of her life.

Mary made other and some perhaps unexpected contributions to life at Keele, notably in connection with the Chapel. She served on the Chapel Committee and drew up a lectionary, tracing the growth of Christian teaching through the Old Testament into the New. There was widespread appreciation of the Sunday School which she founded for her colleagues' children, who were growing up and running around the campus. The students who volunteered to help in this enterprise derived as much enjoyment and stimulus as the children from her leadership.

She had a natural gift with children which endeared her too to adults. Her whimsical way of expressing herself enabled her to combine irresistible childish nonsense stories with a presentation of eternal verities, at a child's level, which some of her listeners say they will never forget.

It was at Keele, in her lectures on social developments in the 18th and 19th centuries, that Mary became more interested than ever in the plight of the wretchedly poor, and the harsh attitudes adopted towards poverty by the authorities of the time. She was specially moved by the brutalising punishments inflicted by the courts even for minor offences, and this led to her increasing interest in penal reform and later on in the treatment of the insane.

In retirement, she and Professor Dorothy Emmet helped Sir Walter Moberley in the final stages of his publication on *The Theory of Punishment*. At the same time, her mind was still moving more and more to the underlying causes of social problems, ignorance, lack of understanding, and indeed man's seeming innate cruelty, that bring misery to so many. Thus during her retirement she was led to researching into the treatment of the mentally sick, and so, by courtesy of the Governors and the Medical Director of The Retreat at York, to a close study of The Retreat archives and a growing admiration for the Tuke family and their colleagues. The writing of this short book occupied her closing years. It became her major and absorbing occupation, but progressive illness prevented its completion in her life time. When she died, the material was assembled and much of it written up, but it was not ready for the press. It has been a privilege for us to complete Mary's work.

Cambridge,
March 1984

Janet Glover
and
Elizabeth Glover

Introduction

In 1790 a Quaker widow called Hannah Mills went out of her mind, and her friends brought her to the York Asylum, which had been founded in 1777. As was the Quaker custom, the Friends' Meeting to which she belonged in Leeds wrote to the York Friends to say she was coming to York, and asking them to look her up. This they attempted to do; several times women members of the York Meeting went to the asylum, but they were never allowed to see her. A few months later she died.

York Friends were shocked; they suspected that she had not been well treated. We do not know what the evidence for this was, but such things get about; servants, for instance, often gossip freely. Besides, if you go to an institution to see a friend and are refused admission, the manner in which you are excluded may give a daunting impression of the spirit of the place.

William Tuke, a Quaker tea-merchant, and his family were discussing this event, when his daughter Ann, who was twenty-three, said 'Father, why cannot we have an establishment for such persons in our own Society?' William Tuke was immediately taken with the idea and he never gave it up. His wife who was a strong-minded, outspoken woman, was appalled. She is reported to have said: 'Thee has many wonderful children of thy brain, dear William, but this is surely like to be an idiot-birth'.

But he did not give up the idea and early in 1792 he put to the York Quarterly Meeting a proposal that Friends should set up their own asylum at York. 'A wet blanket was thrown upon the scheme:' so wrote his great-grandson Daniel Hack Tuke. But he persisted, with the help of his son Henry, and in June 1792 a group of Friends founded The Retreat.

It seems that William Tuke's persistence, in face of his wife's reaction, the scepticism which he met with at first in the Society of Friends, and the monstrous difficulties involved, sprang from a sense, even while his daughter Ann was speaking, that this was the Will of God for him. Letters he had written in the 1760's reveal his profound conviction that God does make known His Will and that the Christian is therefore under an absolute obligation to follow it.

He founded The Retreat and its work is recorded in the *Description of the Retreat* by his grandson Samuel Tuke. The difficulties which might have been anticipated as probable, when a tea-merchant of limited means, and no experience of managing the insane, undertakes to run an asylum, did indeed come upon him. But he and his helpers surmounted them.

This book tells the story of how the institution evolved new and far more humane treatment of the mentally ill; it won the astonished and admiring praise of that keen social critic, the Reverend Sydney Smith, and through him of a wide public; it made a powerful impact on the theory and practice of asylums in this country and abroad.

PERSPECTIVE VIEW of the **NORTH FRONT** of the **RETREAT** near **YORK.**

1813

CHAPTER I

The General Condition of the Insane in the 18th Century

THE originality and achievement of The Retreat can best be evaluated against the background of the general conditions to which the insane were exposed in the 18th and early 19th centuries. Accordingly, in this chapter comment is made on the legal position of the insane, also on the main theories current at the time regarding insanity, and how it should be treated.

Misconceived ideas about medical practice had long roots going back through the medieval period to much earlier times and these bore especially hardly on the mentally ill. In Appendix E on page 98 George III's supposed insanity, and the primitive methods adopted to deal with it, are outlined. His illness was much in the public mind at the time when The Retreat was being established, and highlights the importance of what its founders were trying to achieve, for if dreadful things could be done to a King suffering from critical illness, even worse were likely to happen to insane people of lowly social standing.

There was by no means enough legal protection or provision for the insane in the 18th century. Ways of dealing with allegedly mad people had been improvised under laws made with other classes in mind. Destitute people had always been considered the responsibility of the Church, and they were relieved from the parish poor rate, either by money grants from the Overseer of the Poor, or in a workhouse. Many insane people were put into the workhouse, along with the destitute, and their behaviour there was one of the distasteful conditions the sane inhabitants had to put up with. Vagrants found wandering and unemployed outside their own parish could be confined in bridewells, and a homeless lunatic could be so dealt with. Lunatics who broke the law came under the provisions of the general criminal law. Whipping, transportation or hanging were prescribed for many crimes. The death penalty applied to more than two hundred offences, some of them incredibly trivial, at the end of the 18th century. As regards lunatics, confinement in a bridewell for a minor offence was normal, but the death penalty, even for murder, was not invariable if the offender was believed insane.

1

The earliest, and for long the only asylum for the mentally ill, was Bethlem in London. It had been founded in 1247 as a priory of the Order of St. Mary of Bethlehem; in 1377 it became an institution for the acutely insane. Its name got worn down to Bethlem and then Bedlam. This change tells a story; Bedlam became one of the sights of London; young men would take their girl-friends there of a Sunday to be diverted by the maniacs, for a charge of 2d per head. If the patients were withdrawn or lethargic, the keepers would prod them with sticks to enrage them so that their betters could have their money's worth of fun.

Very many of the insane were living in their own homes. There they must have been a humiliating nuisance, needing to be kept under control and out of sight. The simplest way to confine a lunatic and prevent him from straying, is to chain him. A working woman for instance, obliged to leave her demented husband at home while she went out to earn a wage to support him, might do this; and if he made a difficulty about the chaining, it would save a lot of trouble to keep the padlock locked. In the houses of the well-to-do, it would be possible to set aside a room for the patient and his attendant; in poorer homes it might be necessary to confine him under the stairs or in a shed.

Where there is a great need and inadequate public provision for it, private enterprise may fill the gap; many private madhouses came into existence. Some of these were managed with good sense and kindness; such places were a great boon to Charles and Mary Lamb and to the poet Cowper, but many were appalling places full of noise and smells and brutal punishment.

It had been assumed that certain classes of human beings, soldiers for instance and sailors, prisoners, children, especially boys, and lunatics could only be controlled by cruelty, but public feeling was changing and influential people becoming uneasy. In the 18th century humanitarian feeling was gaining on traditional thought and practice; many of our great hospitals were founded, and orphanages and almshouses; there was concern about prisons and about poverty: and the treatment of the insane troubled many people.

In 1774 an Act was passed to bring madhouses under the control of law. Its provisions were that madhouses could be run for profit only by persons licensed by Commissioners, responsible to Parliament: that such houses should notify the Commissioners of the reception of persons alleged to be insane; that the Commissioners should visit them regularly and see that nobody was unlawfully detained; that those who were detained should be treated properly, under the supervision of a medical man. This Act was wrestling with three difficulties. The first was the need to protect the public against the lunatic. The second was the need to protect members of the public against unjustified confinement as lunatics when they were in fact sane. There was widespread fear, then and much later, that it was far too easy if you had a relative whom you wanted to get out of the way for any reason, to have him confined as insane and never heard of any more. The third difficulty was to secure decent and humane conditions for those who really were insane and had to be confined.

Some forty years later, in 1815 and 1816, the Commissioners under this Act gave evidence to the Select Committee on Madhouses. It appears that they had been conscientious in visitation, but that little had been achieved. It was still the case that very many patients were chained or manacled; it was common practice to starve them to reduce their strength. Often these madhouses were filled with stench, and some Commissioners gave it as their opinion that this was inevitable because where there were so many male patients, some would certainly be incontinent and neither they nor their bedding could be properly cleaned. In some institutions it seems however that this problem was partly overcome by washing the patients, destroying the straw on which they slept, and airing the rooms. Patients in madhouses were constantly subject to beatings and cruelty. There was often uproar from angry patients who were chained and loud ravings from those whose dementia had reached a peak of maniacal fury. It was a common conviction that lunatics were impervious to cold and to punishment. John Haslam, apothecary at Bethlem Hospital from 1795 till 1816, noted that he believed the insane hardened themselves against physical cruelty, and could be more easily controlled by wounding their self-respect. Haslam's evidence to the Select Committee of 1815 and 1816 was lengthy, detailed, and very disturbing. His book, *Observations on Madness and Melancholy* (1809), showed that he had been well aware for some time of the cruelties practised by many keepers, both at Bethlem and also elsewhere. It was clear to the Select Committee that the Commissioners, for all their conscientiousness, had been unable to produce effective improvements. This was because the Act of 1774 had no teeth. Proprietors of madhouses could lose their licence if they refused admission to Commissioners, but there was no way of effectively cancelling a licence, if the licensee repeatedly declined to make any changes required by the Commissioners. It took many years of persistent pressure from reformers before legislation in 1828 made it impossible for the grosser forms of cruelty in madhouses to be allowed.

But it would be a mistake to suppose that places run for profit were uniformly bad. Most people who work are working for pay, and a great many are conscientious. Thomas Bakewell gave evidence to the Select

Committee about the way he ran the madhouse he inherited from his father, and it would appear that he was a sensible and humane man; and he says that on any ride from his house he would be likely to meet former patients or members of their families, who would be glad to see him.

Some explanation of the inhumanity that often characterised the treatment of lunatics can be found by examining how people thought about insanity.

It takes an effort of mind to get over the repulsiveness of the abnormal. People shy away from contact with anybody in great pain, or in great grief. The insane are abnormal, and people do not instantly feel confident that they can understand or deal with them. There had been in the past a dominant theory that they were devil-possessed. There is nothing silly about this, given that there is an established belief in the reality of the devil. Some forms of madness to this day make it difficult, for the ordinary observer, not to believe in devil-possession. Dr. John Conolly, a man who was devoted to the cause of the insane, and who spent most of his professional life studying their problems, was in charge of an institution at Hanwell from 1839 till 1856. Much reference will be made to him in this book. His published works on the treatment of the insane give invaluable information about conditions in the first half of the 19th century. Writing as late as 1860, Dr. Conolly records the harm he thinks was done to his patients by a sermon, preached in chapel, on the theme that 'madness is a spiritual disease and the chief work of the devil.'

In the 18th century the prevailing idea was that the mentally ill had become somehow sub-human and insensitive, that they were in fact a species of animal, filthy, comic, often dangerous. This also is not an irrational idea, the behaviour of the insane can be terrifying, and often incredibly senseless.

When William Tuke and his committee began their experiment at The Retreat, they were very ready to learn from the experience and teaching of others, who knew more about the management of asylums. The books they read, the hospitals they visited, all seemed to say the same thing, namely that the first principle in handling the insane was to instil fear; as soon as the patient arrived one had to get an ascendancy over him by daunting him. William's grandson, Samuel Tuke, who visited a number of asylums, saw this system in action, and admitted that it brought results, though he found no justification for the practices he witnessed. He wrote: 'There is a considerable class of patients, whose eccentricities may in great measure be controlled, and who may be kept in subjection and apparent orderly habits, by the strong excitement of the principle of fear. They may be made to obey their keepers with the greatest promptitude: to rise, to sit, to stand, to walk or run, at their pleasure; though only expressed by a look. Such obedience, and even the appearance of affection, we not infrequently see in the poor animals who are exhibited to gratify our interest in natural history . . . the result of treatment at which humanity should shudder'. This regime of terror was maintained by punishment, by physical restraint and sometimes by insolence of manner. The psychology of fear was not properly understood. Dr. Cullen, for instance, in 1784 wrote, 'Fear being a passion that diminishes excitement . . . it has appeared to me necessary to employ a very constant impression (of it) . . . and therefore to inspire (patients) with awe and dread of some particular person, especially of those who are to be constantly near them. This awe and dread . . . to be acquired in the first place by their being the authors of all the restraints that may be occasionally proper, but sometimes it may be necessary to acquire it even by stripes and blows . . . Restraining the anger and violence of madmen is always necessary for preventing their hurting themselves or others; but this restraint is also considered as a remedy'. But of course Dr. Cullen and those who thought as he did were wrong. Fear does sometimes induce cowering and quietness, as Samuel Tuke noted, but it sometimes excites. Those who deal with animals know that a scared animal is often more dangerous than a confident one; the same is true of men. Fear and anger are close akin and both may release adrenalin into the blood stream, so that the creature, man or beast, becomes more ferocious and more dangerous.

It was natural for keepers to be afraid of the insane, because they were often physically powerful and when they became violent they were a danger. Sedation was in those days almost unknown, indeed the only effective drug for this purpose in the 18th and early 19th century was founded on opium or laudanum, and doctors disliked resorting to it, because it was addictive — though it was used in Mother Seager's Soothing Syrup to quieten babies.

The alternative was to use instruments of mechanical restraint, chains, straitwaistcoats, leglocks and countless others. Hanwell Hospital was founded in 1831, and when Dr. John Conolly took up his appointment there in 1839, he found 600 such instruments, and they were in constant use, till after a very few months, he made stringent regulations against them. 'A patient is angry and strikes; he is restless and tears his clothes; he runs about with inconvenient activity, and his arms and legs are tied or fastened by handcuffs or leglocks or straps or a leather muff or straitwaistcoat . . . Or the patient is . . . desponding, disinclined to take food, weary even of life and inclined to hang himself. Without respect to the state of his brain which is diseased, all these results of malady are equally met by brutal force, which increases the malady. If patients are unable to keep themselves clean they are placed in what is termed a restraint-chair, which is in fact a permanent close-stool; and if they are fidgety when so disposed of, their hands are tied to the arms of the chair and their feet restrained by straps to the lower part of it . . . A patient in restraint cannot dress or undress himself, cannot keep himself clean, cannot relieve his weary and pained muscles by change of posture . . . Straw beds are not always clean, and scanty diet leads to ulcerations, which are neglected . . . To all these things older officers of asylums become so accustomed that many of them saw them daily without any effort to put an end to what seemed to be hopeless. The attendants became careless . . . dirt and noise and violence prevailed in the kitchens, in the laundries, in the workshops'. Dr. John Conolly says that whenever the straitwaistcoat is put on a patient, he objects and yells and all the patients become tense and troubled. John Haslam, the apothecary at Bethlem, described the effect of the straitwaistcoat to the Select Committee: 'If the waistcoat be tied tightly, respiration is prevented or impeded, and it is always at the mercy of the keeper how tightly he chooses to tie it. If the patient is itching in any part . . . if troubled with flies . . ., if it is not changed, it is liable to absorb a great deal of perspiration, which renders the skin excoriated, he cannot wipe his nose and becomes a driveller in consequence; he cannot assist himself in the evacuation of his urine or his faeces'.

It would be wrong, however, to give the impression that patients in madhouses run for profit were never well-treated. Charles and Mary Lamb, who had experience of such houses, did not complain of cruelty, though Mary said what the patient needed most was tenderness, and that was more 'than could be expected of a paid woman'. A straitwaistcoat could be used without violence; Mary Lamb made it a practice never to take a journey without her waistcoat, in case she should become disturbed. In his book *Trade in Lunacy, a study of Madhouses in England in the 18th and 19th centuries*, Dr. W. Ll. Parry-Jones makes it clear that standards in these madhouses depended upon who was running them, and therefore these standards could vary from excellence to wretchedness.

And yet it is saddening to realise as one studies the records, that the sufferings of the insane went far beyond what could be excused as reaction to difficulties inherent in their condition, or forgivable ineptitude in handling them, or fear. Some of it would seem to have been due to the resentment of the keepers, whose own conditions of life and living would have been most unenviable, and who would have found it almost impossible not to turn their anger against their patients.

There is also another pervasive fact to bear in mind. This is human inertia. Dr. Conolly recalled his astonishment as a student observing senior doctors at work. 'I used to be astonished (in 1833) to see humane physicians going daily round the wards of asylums, mere spectators of every form of distressing coercion, without a word of sympathy, or any order for its mitigation. But men's hearts on this subject become gradually hardened'.

Ordinary people when they become aware of such things, tend to shrug their shoulders and say, often erroneously, 'Well, it can't be helped'. Even trained people become inured to witnessing pain. The fact is it would demand great expenditure of energy to get such things altered. One surprising example of this is the case of John Haslam, the apothecary already referred to, who 'reigned supreme' at Bethlem. If one reads his books, and his evidence to the Select Committee, they appear to bear witness to a sensitive, observant and resourceful man, but in 1816 at the age of 52 he was dismissed on the ground that he had allowed unnecessary and shocking cruelty to go on unchecked at Bethlem, where there were officials under his authority who permitted and practised such violence against patients. It is interesting that John Haslam is said to have had no difficulty in at once building up a private practice, after his dismissal, and that in 1816 Aberdeen University awarded him a doctorate

It would appear that during the earlier part of the eighteenth century, doctors had very little to do with the treatment of the insane. The upper class of medical men were members of the Royal Society of Physicians. There were very few of them, and they tended to think of 'maniacal practice' as 'so forlorn a study' as to be fit only 'for the coercive attendant'. Ordinary people were treated when sick by apothecaries, men of humbler status in society, trained by working under senior practitioners in the use of herbal and other simple medicines, also in such forms of light surgery as bleeding. One's impression is that some of them at least may have been more effective than physicians because they were so constantly with their patients. Some of these patients must have been in a condition that would now be called mental illness; but they were then likely to be diagnosed as highly nervous, or melancholic or excitable. Apothecaries felt it to be part of their professional duty to give comfort and personal counsel as well as medicines.

The approach of medical men was influenced by Galen. He was physician to the Emperor Marcus Aurelius in the second century A.D. It is surprising that so ancient an authority still carried so much weight, but the fact is that until much later than this, scholarship in many academic subjects was based on an overpowering reverence for the classical writers of Greece and Rome. Knowledge of Galen was kept alive by the fact that any M.A. of Oxford or Cambridge could qualify as a physician by delivering a few lectures on Galen, who was a prolific writer. Much of his teaching was of a still older date, for he generally followed the teaching of Hippocrates of Cos, a Greek doctor who lived and taught about seven hundred years before the time of Galen. He ran a medical school, and he devised and required of his students the famous Hippocratic oath, which doctors of today do not formally 'take', but accept as setting forth our own ideal of a doctor.

Hippocrates thought like a scientist; he taught his students to keep case notes, and to base their prognosis of the course an illness would take on the experience accumulated in these notes. He was much interested in the effect of climate on disease, and lectured on this and other subjects with acumen. His treatment was mainly what would be called today 'a conservative regime'. The patient was to be kept quiet, in a shaded room, on a low diet, with little medication and almost no surgery. He was so successful by this method that he attracted the criticism of Plato. Plato held that any rational man would rather take his chance with surgery or cautery and perhaps die, than be kept alive as an invalid. Hippocrates however also had a theory which he taught his students, namely that health is a proper balance of the fluids (or humours) of the body, (blood, water, bile and phlegm) and disease an imbalance. This theory, which is false, lasted much longer than his practice which was good; and Galen accepted the age-old theory of *The Humours*.

At the time The Retreat was founded, when William Tuke and his physician, Timothy Maud, were reading books and visiting hospitals in order to learn as much as they could about the treatment of the insane, they discovered a dominant orthodoxy, which based medical treatment on what was roughly dehydration, the draining away of fluid out of the body. For this purpose a number of methods were used, bleeding, vomits, purges, and blisters. In many hospitals these treatments were a matter of routine. Dr. Monro, the physician at Bethlem, gave evidence to the Select Committee of 1816 describing the practice there. 'They are ordered to be bled about the latter end of May, or the beginning of May, according to the weather; and after they have been bled they take vomits once a week for a certain number of weeks, after that we purge the patients; that has been the practice invariably for years, long before my time; it was handed down to me by my father, and I do not know any better practice'. A naval hospital for the insane was criticised for not using these treatments. A letter from William Tuke to William Maud, son of Timothy Maud, dated February 1798 speaks of it in use at The Retreat. 'James Fawcett has bn v bad. Frequently high and noisy. He made gt efforts for mastery, and if in his power would have done a mischief to those about him, but for some days past has bn pretty quiet .... he was bled in the arm; had a pretty strong Emetic and Cathartic, also a blister, and since that was bled with leaches.' (sic).

Patients were then as now sometimes treated by shock, but the 18th century shocks were cruder. One of them was 'the bath of surprise'; the patient fell without warning through a trap door into cold deep water. Another in common use was the revolving chair; the patient was strapped into the chair which was then whirled around until he lost consciousness. This was unimaginably cruel, strictly speaking *unimaginably*. When mental patients were subjected to this the experience must have been traumatic in the extreme; it was continued not merely till they screamed, but until they passed out. It must be remembered that the sensation *is* unimaginable; those who ordered it and the attendants who carried it out had no slightest conception of what they were doing. They may well have thought the panic shrieking was itself evidence of insanity; it was not, it was evidence of normality. But whether it was possible for anyone who was put through it to recover normality after such prolonged mortal terror, which actually caused unconsciousness, is not recorded.

By the end of the 18th century, there were some doctors, isolated from each other, and therefore largely unaware of what new thinking was developing, who were coming round to the idea that all this harshness was not the best way to deal with patients. Dr. Ferriar wrote in *Medical Histories and Reflexions* (1795) that although when the mentally ill were 'in the furious state, the arms and sometimes the legs must be confined, . . . this should never be done when it can possibly be avoided'. He describes how by 'remonstration' with a patient he could get him quiet 'for lunatics often have a high sense of honour'. However Ferriar's next comment is significant, as it shows that even he was at a loss to find effective humane treatment. He says lunatics 'are sooner brought to reflexion by the appearance of indignity than by actual violence against which they usually harden themselves', but Ferriar emphasised that 'a system of discipline, mild but firm, which makes a patient sensible of restraint without exciting pain or terror, is best suited to these complaints'. We have no evidence that Dr. Ferriar's work was known to the founders of The Retreat at the time when they were embarking on their project.

Another example of efforts to treat the mentally ill with less violence is to be found in the records of Dr. Edward Fox, who ran a small-asylum at Cleve Hill, in Downend, Bristol from 1794. He opened a larger one at Brislington House in 1806 and he made a point of trying to give his patients as nearly normal a pattern of daily routines as he could. The Retreat was later to owe much to Dr. Fox because one of his staff, Katherine Allen, after a short period of training at Cleve Hill, moved on to The Retreat, and there she became very influential.

9

It is important to understand the quandary the doctors were in. They had at the end of the 18th century very limited knowledge of anatomy, physiology and pathology, and apparently none at all of the great variety of mental illnesses to which the human race can succumb, and they had access to the use of very few drugs. Until research had publicised much more accurate and detailed understanding of the many forms which mental illness can take, doctors — even those in charge of institutions for the so-called insane — were hard put to it to find appropriate treatments. Even people so enlightened as those who founded The Retreat wrote and spoke of their patients as if they were all suffering in some degree or other from the same sort of affliction. Twentieth century doctors and patients are living in a completely different situation, and it is all too easy to criticise what went on a hundred to a hundred and fifty years ago.

The surprising thing is that in some institutions, of which The Retreat is an outstanding and very early example, new and better methods *were* gradually developed early in the 19th century, and these attracted immense interest.

The story of what The Retreat did to change the thinking of a whole generation on the difficult matter of insanity will not be fully understood without some reference to the Quaker tradition, which inspired William Tuke. The next chapter is designed to give some insight into this.

CHAPTER II

Quakerism

THE Quaker movement which inspired William Tuke was founded by George Fox who was born in 1624. Its basis is the belief that God can and does communicate directly with people through their hearts and minds. The Quakers built upon this a philosophy of religion, an order of worship and a way of life. It is a thoroughly Biblical faith. The experience of direct awareness of God, of God's fully personal communication with men, has been known again and again in the history of mankind; it is an authentic abiding element in the human experience of God. What is distinctively Quaker is the belief that knowledge and experience of God is not dependent upon an ordained priesthood or ritual sacraments.

Thus, of course, Quakers found themselves in head-on collision with Church and State. Charles I and those who thought with him regarded toleration as a very dangerous idea; the King loved the Church of England and was convinced that the abandonment of episcopacy as the unquestioned authority must inevitably lead to heresies, extravagances and dangerous divisions within the nation. He was not wrong in this. Hence the long attempt to destroy freedom of worship; hence persecution and martyrdom, for some Quakers and also for many others.

The Quakers, like other Dissenters, formed their own congregations and met for worship according to their own ideas. Such meetings were illegal until the Act of Toleration in 1689. So the first generation of Quakers often worshipped in one another's houses, well aware that they might be invaded at any minute by soldiers and carried off to prison, where they would not have an easy time. In fact their chief executive meeting was, and is, called the Meeting for Sufferings, dating back to the time when its chief business was to take action to relieve the distress not only of those imprisoned but also of their families.

In his book, *The Quakers, their story and message*, published by Sessions, 1982, A. Neave Brayshaw gives on page 167 a summary of the organisation developed by Quakers. He says that each congregation forms a Preparative Meeting for the management of its own affairs: that a group of Preparative Meetings forms a Monthly Meeting — the executive body in a particular district — while several Monthly Meetings form a Quarterly Meeting (nowadays known as a General Meeting). The number of Quarterly Meetings was organised as a Yearly Meeting, the legislative body of the whole. In England the Yearly Meeting normally took place in London. The name Quaker was originally used by critics of the movement in some contempt, because the early Quakers urged people to tremble at the Word of the Lord. Brayshaw tells us on page 44 (op. cit.) that by 1800 the name 'The Society of Friends' had come into common use.

The Meeting for Worship is conducted in silence, the whole group waiting together upon God. Individuals may be moved to make a spoken contribution or to offer prayer. It is felt that a traditional order of service, still more a legally appointed one, or the leadership of a paid or trained minister, might impede the free movement of the Spirit upon that particular group at that particular time. The sense of the presence and activity of God can be overwhelming. Samuel Tuke (William's grandson) talked to his daughter Maria about his experience of speaking in Meeting. The Tukes were reticent men, but Maria had come very close to her father since his wife's death. Maria records that he spoke of 'that real subjection of the heart which all must experience, if they are to attain true peace. I knew something of it when I first said a few words in Meeting. It seemed then as if *man* was nothing, *Christ* was all; as if the chiefest pleasure was being engaged in His service'. When a man or woman speaks out of this experience, those who hear share in some degree in the sense of the reality of God.

The Quaker way of life was carefully thought out in relation to the Sermon on the Mount. Their literal acceptance of the Sermon on the Mount involved severe trials, of which perhaps the most incessant lay in the injunction 'Swear not at all'. In a semi-literate society oaths were common in the ordinary way of business to conclude a contract, instead of signing; but people quickly discovered that a Quaker's simple 'yes' or 'no' was reliable. At law however the refusal to take the oath could be the cause of punishment for contempt of court. One of the most difficult teachings of the Sermon on the Mount is its pacifism; Quakers believed that the Article of Religion 37, 'that it is lawful for Christian men at the command of the magistrate to wear arms and serve in the wars' was false. What also affected Quakers continually was the command 'Resist not evil'; this they carried out faithfully. They broke the law when their consciences required them to do so and accepted condign punishment without complaint. Thus they refused to pay tithes, because it was against their conscience to support the Church of England, a church they believed to be in error; but they peacefully admitted the bailiff to distrain upon their goods to the amount of the tithe (or more, sometimes). From 1689, the Act of Toleration abolished penalties for free worship, and persecution gradually ceased, but there remained other disabilities such as those connected with tithes and oaths.

From earliest days, the Quakers had frowned on extravagant living. Brayshaw (op. cit., page 202) quotes Fox as follows: '.... that costly apparel with the lace that we formerly had hung upon our backs that kept us not warm, with that we could maintain a company of poor people that had no clothes'. A modest and almost ascetic standard of living was thought right, but by the 18th century a new temptation was assailing Quakers: wealth.

In England the Act of Uniformity of 1662 excluded from the universities all who would not go through the motions of expressing assent to the doctrine of the Church of England. Entry to the professions was through the universities, and thus Quakers and other Nonconformists could not enter the professions. For a time thereafter the Quaker movement seems to have consisted chiefly of rather humble people, as well as tradesmen, manufacturers and bankers. But in the 18th century England was becoming wealthier; many developments contributed to this; the increasing effect of the industrial revolution, the East India Company's trade in Oriental luxuries, the Slave Trade, new methods in agriculture. It seems easier to live simply if you are poor; but it often happens that if you work very hard and spend very little, and are scrupulously honest, however much you disapprove of wealth, wealth will come to you. Sydney Smith in 1813 thought of the Quakers as a rich sect. Although people of very limited means became Quakers, the Gurneys, Barclays, Cadburys, Rowntrees, Frys, Barrows and Harveys were building up their fortunes.

Yearly Meeting issued a series of Yearly Epistles of exhortation inculcating simplicity and indeed asceticism. A passage from the Epistle of 1810 is typical of many. 'A caution to all to use moderation in their manner of living; and in this way to seek relief from the increasing expense of the times in which we live, rather than by engaging in more extensive and often more hazardous schemes in trade. By these latter means the mind becomes encumbered and unfitted for religious service, yea often for religious thought, and for breathing daily after the spiritual riches which are to be enjoyed in close communion with God'.

It was common for Quakers who had 'a concern' about something, a sense that something new or a special step ought to be taken by Quakers, to consult their own Meeting in the first instance. In such consultation, it would be the wish of the Meeting not to give its support to hare-brained or ill-considered projects, but at the same time there would be a pervading acknowledgment of 'that of God in every man' and a sense of responsibility not to kill any idea that might bear fruit. In a time of change, like the late 18th century, when for instance a new concern for social welfare was growing in the Society, it might be a matter of difficult judgment to distinguish between a novel idea and an unrealistic foolish one. One imagines that the gradual development of determined opposition to the Slave Trade and to slavery may have done a good deal to convince people that quite new ideas might not be unrealistic after all, might in fact be the Will of God.

An important and creative aspect of Quaker thinking is the statement in the Gospel of St. John (1 : 9) that 'that was the true light that lighteth every man that cometh into the world'. Quakers believe that there is 'that of God' in everyone, in men, women and children, rich and poor, masters and servants, the learned, the simple and the demented. This fundamental human equality before God they accept as the basis of relationships. Life at The Retreat was to be profoundly affected by this philosophy, worship and way of living. It is a part of Quaker belief acutely relevant to penal codes: a man may have committed a gross crime but there will still be that of God in him, and punishments that batter his spiritual being into nothing, or nearly nothing, must be contrary to the mind of God. Anybody who holds the Quaker faith must be committed to the effort to make contact with that of God in the wrongdoer. The same principle applies to those who have lost the use of their reason.

It was therefore not surprising that William Tuke, once he was convinced that God had service for him to offer to the insane, became committed to a lifelong involvement.

CHAPTER III

William Tuke

WILLIAM Tuke was born in York in 1732. His father Samuel was a stuff-weaver and kept a shop. It was a Quaker family.

One of William's strongest characteristics through life was pertinacity and as a small boy he had an adventure that put this quality to the test.

WILLIAM TUKE from the painting by Henry Scott Tuke, R.A.

Henry Scott Tuke was a great great-grandson of William Tuke, born thirty six years after William's death (1822). He must have worked from another painting, possibly a miniature, of which there is no record.

15

He went birds'-nesting and fell out of the tree. He found he had hurt his leg and tried to get home by hopping; but he had hurt his head too, and the hopping movement gave him too much pain in the head to bear. However, he got home. Since he ought not to have been in the tree he decided to say nothing about the matter. Then he found his head was bleeding, so he put his hat on again. Hats were often worn indoors, and this did not attract comment. But there came into the shop a customer who had seen him fall, and asked if he was all right; so his mother found out what had happened and sent for the doctor. The doctor said the boy's head must be trephined; this meant removing a small piece of bone from the skull. It probably had to be done without an anaesthetic and one does not know how long the operation took. Surgeons prided themselves on their speed in operating. In his later life, William's grandchildren loved to clamber over him and feel over his head with their delicate fingers for the soft place which the trephining had left.

His father died when he was 16 and his mother seven years later. But from his childhood he had been much under the care of his aunt and uncle, Mary and Henry Frankland. Henry was an active Friend, said to have been a man of difficult temper, but he died when the boy was eight. William had good schooling, for two or three years in a boarding school; later he was tutored by a clergyman and he learnt some Latin. When he was 14 he was apprenticed to his aunt, Mary Frankland, who had a small grocery shop at the corner of Castlegate and Coppergate. Mary Frankland was an intrepid character: for years she sustained a running fight with the York Merchant Adventurers, who, since she was not a member of their company, contested her right to sell at retail, but because she was neither the daughter nor the widow of a Freeman they would not admit her to membership. She was fined heavily several times, but in 1732 settled to pay a fee of ten shillings a year and was permitted to trade, on condition that she bought all her stock in York and took no apprentices. These conditions must have been lifted or ignored later.

Another vexation continued. As a Quaker she refused to pay Church tithes, and a bailiff would call to distrain upon the shop, without too nice a regard for what she owed. William recorded that on one occasion when the unpaid tithe amounted to twelve shillings and sevenpence, they took twelve shillings and ten pence from the till and also six and a half pounds of lump sugar. Another time when William was alone in the shop, the warrant was for eight shillings and nine pence and they took goods to precisely that value.

Mary Frankland, a childless widow, became an invalid. William was always a kind man and he was good to his aunt. When she died in 1752, before he had quite completed his apprenticeship to her, she left him her business, the premises, the stock, the good will and some other properties. William was then 19. He realised that this legacy gave him a new freedom, he was not condemned for life to manage groceries in a small corner-shop; he could sell out and go into some other work 'where he would learn more'. But friends persuaded him to drop this idea and keep the shop.

His ambition then took a different turn; he wanted very much to excel in business, to make his name as a man of wealth, as he said afterwards, 'to be esteemed of men, to live rather high'. He took up his claim to be a Freeman of the City in 1753, and became a York Merchant Adventurer in 1754.

In 1754 he married Elizabeth Hoyland of Sheffield. It was a good marriage; he said of his life with her that 'he supposed few couples had more enjoyment of each other's company'. But they went through difficult times together, partly because Elizabeth, as a good Quaker, thought his desires for wealth and worldly pleasures were wrong, and he, as a bad Quaker (according to his own view), agreed with her, but could not alter the set of his desires; and partly because his business did not always prosper. In one year they 'thought they had kept careful accounts and must have made £100', but when they went into it they found they had made a loss. He was greatly cast down. The conflict between his conscience and his desire for wealth and indulgence, made his wife miserable. He felt she was very good to him, striving for his salvation.

In 1760 Elizabeth was expecting her fifth child, in her sixth year of marriage, and she had a presentiment of death. William says 'I imputed it only to fears which are usual in such cases' and thought she was pretty well. But Elizabeth did die in childbed. 'I was almost on the brink of destruction when my dear wife was taken from me, and in such manner that I could see no cause for it but divine judgment on me.' William's grandson Samuel said he thought the loss of Elizabeth was 'the Bethel of his life, the place of prayers and vows'. From what William said later it would seem that this was so. He found release from the overwhelming burden of grief and remorse in the thought that God sustained him, that 'underneath was the everlasting arm'; and that he must mobilise all his will-power to become obedient to the will of God. This he did. He abandoned the ambition to be a rich man, and never was rich though he perhaps cultivated a gift for appearing well-to-do. In the years that followed he did become a leading Quaker, and his generosity to all sorts of projects designed for welfare of one sort and another was one of his outstanding characteristics.

For some years William Tuke had been acquainted, through his work for the Society of Friends, with a family called Maud, who in 1763 lived in Bradford. William met Esther Maud at Quarterly Meeting and she impressed him very much. She had gifts of leadership, men found her 'queenly' and she had great influence with young people. She and William corresponded, and in 1764 he asked her to marry him, and long letters were then exchanged. He told her, with rare self-revelation, about his moral conflicts, his grave faults in the past and about his religious experience. She replied with equal candour and said she could not bring herself 'to attempt to lessen or disguise a regard I have long by words and actions manifested', but she did not expect to be able to marry him, because she was supporting her family. She went on to tell him of her own grievous experience, of her ne'er-do-well brother: he had greatly impoverished the family and then disappeared to America, where he died, leaving heavy debts which her father had not been able to pay off; she felt this trouble had cost her father his life. She had then taken up the burden, paid off the debts, and was now supporting her mother and younger brother and sister. She spoke of the deep despair that had engulfed her; she had an oppressive sense of sin, though she seems to have been a very good and brave woman.

William wrote back with great sympathy, suggesting that her brother and sister could now manage for themselves and that it would be for their good; and that if she married him, her mother could join his household: he did not pretend that this would be very agreeable, but he thought it could be endured. He told her his financial position, feeling that she had a right to know that it was not as good as she might have supposed; he reckoned he was worth between £600 and £700, and had some reliable business connections. And then he said, 'but sure scarce any ever formed greater schemes in ideas than I, nor perhaps any more unfit to be trusted with affluence'. This candour to the woman he wanted to marry is evidence of the confidence they already had in each other.

He wrote later: 'I have always found the greatest freedom and inclination towards thee when my mind has been most nearly united to the fountain of all good . . . I can only request of thee not to suffer the reasoning part too much to take place, but principally regard the directions and leading of truth, and I desire to do so too . . . I salute thee most affectionately, thy true William'. His point here is not a contrast between reason and emotion; he is not saying, 'Marry me if you love me, that is the main thing'. He is thinking that we may reach one conclusion when we argue a matter out with careful common sense calculation, and another when we attend to the Inner Light; and urges her to marry him if her own inward guidance leads her to him. We have here a clue to the principles which governed his habitual thinking and decision-making.

After due consideration she did find a true liberty to join him, and they were married on June 3rd 1765 in the Meeting House at Bradford. In the event Mrs. Maud went to live with her other daughter, and William had Esther to himself.

He had, however, to share her with his family of five, Henry aged 10, and Sarah, William, John and Elizabeth. The children did not at first welcome their stepmother; especially Sarah, who had been four or five when her mother died, and was now nine. This gallant little girl had apparently accepted an intimate responsibility to her father which she did not find easy to surrender, William must have depended on her a great deal.

Esther won the affection of the children mainly for a rather surprising reason; she was irresistibly amusing. They had not wished to like her, but she made them laugh, and they did. We have this on the very reliable authority of Samuel Tuke, Henry's son. 'She was lively and spirited and had a natural facetiousness which made young people greatly enjoy her society', he wrote. It is interesting that William married a woman with such a gift for appreciating the comic side of things: he does not seem to have had a strong sense of humour himself, nor does anybody else in his circle, until Esther's daughter Mabel was born. Of her Sarah did not quite approve; she thought her too flighty. Esther and William had a son in 1767, when Esther was 39, but he died a year old. In 1768 they had a daughter Ann, and three years later Mabel.

William and Esther devoted themselves to the Quaker cause. Esther used to go on preaching journeys to visit Monthly and Quarterly Meetings, and William sometimes accompanied her. They found a degree of aridity and deadness widespread in the Society which distressed them. Samuel Tuke in his *Memoirs* says that at this time the Society 'had come in many places (and truly York was not an exception) to be managed not only by a few, but also by dry formal members, wholly unable to sympathise with the awakened, or with those who err and are out of the way . . .' He saw that laxity, partiality, formality and perhaps spiritual pride had crept into its proceedings . . . 'My grandfather's spirit was stirred within him . . . the old men treated his expostulations with contempt, telling the Clerk not to mind what he said'. William, having overcome great moral difficulty in his own life, was more outspoken on what he felt was 'laxity' in others than was welcome.

One of the things William castigated as laxity was the wearing of smuggled shawls by Quaker women. One can't help sympathising with these women; they had to dress so plainly, and they needed shawls because they had no other protection in bad weather. The East India Company was importing these and other novelties, the import duties were high, there was every inducement to smuggle. When a man came to the door with exotic and beautiful shawls at a surprisingly low price, no wonder the housewife wanted to buy. When her husband came home and realised that the thing must have been 'run', the man had gone and the wife had the shawl. It is reported that some women left the Society because they took umbrage at William Tuke's protest.

William Tuke's standing in the Society was improved, when a visiting commission, appointed by Yearly Meeting to carry out a visitation of many Meetings in different parts of the country, emphatically endorsed his pressure for stricter adherence to Quaker principles. As a result of this visitation many members withdrew from the Society. Meanwhile the Tukes gradually overcame the unpopularity which their criticisms had excited. In all, William must have been a regular attender at York Meeting for some 60 years, for at least 20 of which he was its Treasurer. For about half a century he made the annual visit to London for Yearly Meeting, and during most of that period it would have taken him at least 40 to 50 hours of travelling time each way on horseback like Wesley, making on average perhaps 3 to 4 miles an hour. By 1771, he was exerting an important influence at Yearly Meeting. There were then speakers who 'called in question the divine character and offices of our Lord'; and William Tuke was foremost in opposing these views. In 1783 he was for one year Clerk of Yearly Meeting; it was not usual then for anybody to hold this office for more than one year. He was greatly gifted in leadership and must have enjoyed it. But it was noted that if he argued strongly for some point, and then found the Meeting against it, he accepted the sense of the Meeting with good grace. During all these years, the family tea business in York was naturally a prime responsibility, and William was fortunate in his son, Henry, who became a partner in 1785, at the age of 30, after 15 years' solid service in the firm.

William and Esther apparently came to feel that if the Society was to win a more inspiring leadership, this must come from the rising generation. But there was a weakness in Quaker handling of their young people. It would seem that they left them without sufficient instruction. This is apparent in the diaries of Elizabeth Gurney (who became Elizabeth Fry). She wrote that she had no ideas about religion whatever; and she could not help thinking that she might live a better life if she could come by some religious belief. The two hours she spent with her family at Meeting in Goat Lane every Sunday, contemplating her purple boots with scarlet laces, gave her no help at all. Eventually she was deeply inspired by a visiting American Quaker, William Savory.

In the 1770's a number of Quakers came to think that boarding schools were needed for children whose parents were, as the 1777 Yearly Meeting put it 'not in affluent circumstances'. It was in 1777 that Dr. Fothergill found an empty house at Ackworth about 25 to 30 miles from York, which had been built for Coram's Foundation, the London Foundling Hospital, but for some reason was not being used for this purpose. It was a fine building, and Dr. Fothergill and his supporters thought it suitable for the newly planned Quaker school for boys and girls. Yearly Meeting approved the scheme, and set up two Committees to run it, a London Committee and a country one; William Tuke was a member of the latter and was present at its first meeting in 1778.

The idea of a school did not at first find support. A minute of York Meeting for the date 29.xi.78 records: 'It does not appear that any incline at present to subscribe towards the establishment of a school at Ackworth'. But those who wanted the school, like good Quakers, persisted. They raised £7,000 to pay for it and the school was opened in 1779. It was immediately a success. Within a year the numbers rose to 256, and two years later a total of £10,000 had been subscribed. William Tuke sent his own younger daughters there, Ann for one year and Mabel for four. William gave an immense amount of time to Ackworth, which he visited almost every week, leaving his son Henry to manage the family business. Today Ackworth School gives a sound, excellent education in its much extended premises, being one of the nine Quaker Boarding Schools in existence.

But by 1784 Esther Tuke was feeling that more should be done; there was a need for 'guarded' education for girls in York. She found some support and though she was not in good health, she opened a small school of her own in 1785. She was its first headmistress. A house was bought in Trinity Lane, and Esther and William left their home over the shop in Castlegate and moved into it. They became jointly the school's first superintendents, or 'caretakers', as their grandson Samuel called them. They furnished their own rooms, paid for their board and took no salary. The teaching assistants, William's daughter Elizabeth and later his and Esther's daughters Ann and Mabel, with two others, also had no salary. The only paid person was a young woman who came in to teach needlework for a small sum.

The brochure, which published the foundation of the school, announced that instruction would be given 'in useful Needlework,

Knitting, the English Language, Writing and Arithmetic'. The girls would have learnt to read, but not necessarily to write, at home.

In spite of the narrowness of the syllabus it proved beyond the competence of the young teachers. They said they could not teach grammar. With all their preference for practical subjects, the Quakers respected the English language and knew it needed to be taught, and that the foundation for competence in using it was knowledge of grammar. It is not an easy subject, but a delightful solution to this impasse was found. Lindley Murray, an American friend of the Tukes, agreed to teach the teachers. For some months in winter, regularly when the day's work was done, these young women put on their pattens and shawls and trudged forth on the half-hour walk in the dark, accompanied by a man with a lantern, to Lindley Murray's house on Holdgate Hill. He was by now an invalid and had a weak voice. He must have found this intrusion of jolly young women very welcome. The girls themselves enjoyed their English Grammar lessons immensely and the schoolgirls whom they taught began to like the subject and to find it intelligible. When the course was over the teachers begged Lindley Murray to publish it and also to publish, in separate covers, a set of exercises and answers to them. Lindley Murray's *English Grammar* is one of the dullest books I have ever looked into, but it met a felt want and was a great success for many years. George Eliot, in chapter 24 of *Middlemarch*, gives us an agreeable picture of Mrs. Garth simultaneously making pastry and teaching English Grammar to her children, Bert and Letty, from Lindley Murray. It was characteristic of Murray that he handed his royalties on the first edition to the Quakers as a contribution towards Ackworth's expenses.

This 'guarded' education, which went on without holidays for a year at a time or more, must one feels have been dreary. But one of the girls wrote home to say that the head was 'like a princess'. They joined the Tukes often of an evening for reading aloud, and must thus have got to know two very interesting people.

But Esther's health did not improve; she found her illness a heavy burden to bear, and she died in 1794. Her school was carried on by the Tuke family till 1812. By that time more than 500 pupils had passed through it. Samuel's comment is: 'I have no doubt that the longing desires of the caretakers were often, or seemed to themselves to be, disappointed'. But in his judgment the enterprise was a success. Part of its success was that the memory of it inspired Friends to put to York Quarterly Meeting in 1831, a proposal that a school for girls should be re-established. This school has been known as The Mount since 1857, when it moved to a house of that name in Dalton Terrace. Like Ackworth, The Mount has a great history and still flourishes.

If William Tuke never became rich, what is more surprising is that he never went bankrupt. Esther once told Mary Maria Scott, who later married Henry Tuke, that she had a constant anxiety about whether they would be able to make ends meet when they did their annual accounts. Many circumstances suggest that bankruptcy could have overtaken William. As a young man, when he inherited the shop, he found the business boring, and seriously considered getting rid of it. Then, as he said, he and Elizabeth tried to keep the accounts carefully and found they were far out, and had 'gone back'. And how could anybody make much money out of buying tea wholesale in London, transporting it to York by pack-horse, and then distributing it wholesale as far as Bristol and Birmingham, also by pack-horse? The East India Company had the monopoly of selling tea till 1834, and up to that date all the tea-clippers sailed for the Port of London.

In addition to the difficulties of the business, there was in him and his family that strong impulse to generosity, which Mary Maria noted with astonishment. 'They are marvellously delivered from this world's wisdom, falsely called prudence.'

The most dangerous factor in William Tuke's finances seems to have been that he did not give his whole mind to his business. If a small business is to succeed, it generally needs to have the unremitting attention of its head. William Tuke was always willing to give his time away to Quaker Meetings, to Ackworth School, to the building of the new Ouse bridge, on religious journeys with his wife, and above all to The Retreat. For nearly a year he was obliged to run The Retreat himself; a far heavier demand upon him than he had ever intended.

Why did this under-capitalised business, begun in a small corner shop, not founder, as William more and more neglected it in favour of other interests, and yet exercised striking generosity? There seem to have been several reasons, of which the most important was probably the support his family gave him. His first wife, Elizabeth, had helped in the shop, and so no doubt did Esther, till she started her school; she was an experienced business woman. William and Margaret Sessions point out in *The Tukes of York* that she must have had her hands full with five step-children and two of her own. Till 1784 they lived over the shop, so that if Esther was at work in it, she would not be very far away; they kept a servant, and Sarah, the eldest daughter, probably helped to look after the younger children, but there must have been endless pressure on Esther. Very important was the fact that Henry, William's eldest son, who later married Mary Maria Scott, entered the business as an apprentice in 1770. He was then fifteen and had already worked for two years as a teacher. He was interested in medicine, and later became a man of letters, but he gave up most of his life to helping his father in the business, and in 1785 became an active partner. His wife, Mary Maria, whom he married in 1781, was a constant moral support, though an invalid. In 1796, the year The Retreat began, when it made far heavier demands upon William's time than he had expected, Henry's son, Samuel, became an apprentice. He was then thirteen years old and had finished his schooling. His interests also lay in medicine, but like his father he too joined the business. At a time when all documents had to be written out by hand, an obedient small boy, who had neat legible writing, could take a great deal of work off his elders.

From 1785, the year when Henry became a partner, to 1835, the Tuke archives preserve the Quarterly sale catalogues of the East India Company, and also the records of the Tuke firm. The firm had concentrated on tea. This specialisation meant that they were on a rising tide. The East India Company had made tea-drinking a fashionable indulgence of the rich; then the habit spread to the working class, rather to the annoyance of their betters. Much more tea must have been drunk by all classes after 1784, when the Government reduced the duty on it from 100% to 12%, in an effort to stop smuggling. At that time it was reckoned that half the tea trade in the country was 'run', but William Tuke would have nothing to do with tea suspected to have been run.

Tea was not the only luxury drink that was being imported at the end of the eighteenth century. Dr. Johnson was an habitué of the coffee house, and chocolate was becoming a popular cordial. The Tukes had started selling a little Turkish coffee, and West Indian coffee, before Henry became a partner in 1785. In that year they acquired a new property in Coppergate, at the corner of Castlegate, and in the back of the shop in Castlegate adjoining it they set up a small workshop to make cocoa and chocolate. This, as William and Margaret Sessions say, 'was the start of Tuke's Rock cocoa, cocoa shells, nibs and nuts, Tuke's plain and milk chocolate and British Cocoa Coffee'. The business prospered.

William Tuke was a man whom many people found attractive, though there were some who had been annoyed with his determination to get his own way. He was superbly endowed with self-will. He was then living in great self-fulfilment; and a very important aspect of this is that his family accepted his natural dominance with pride, pleasure and affection. He had helped to found Ackworth, which was a success; he did not have fears about money and obviously enjoyed lavish hospitality; he was prepared to listen to his guests. He had not been damaged by his great tribulation in the death of his first wife Elizabeth; he met it head on, with unrestrained tears and remorse; God had become more real to him and he had changed his way of life. Esther was clearly the right wife for him, though I think many men could not have put up with her outspokenness. He could. He listened to what she said and gave her a great deal of support in her own enterprises, notably in agreeing to move into her school and live there at his own expense; but he was not under her domination. Esther said of him, as indeed he said of himself, that he had a mind teeming with ideas; he had more than most men a life that afforded some scope for new ideas and intrepid enterprises. He had won a position of leadership in the Society. One cannot help concluding that he enjoyed it all.

This was the state of his affairs, and his mode of living, when Hannah Mills died in the York Asylum and his daughter Ann suggested that the Friends should have an asylum of their own. One cannot feel suprised that even as Ann was speaking, he felt that this was the Will of God. For thirty years and more it had been his settled principle to be guided by inner conviction, and in this matter, in spite of many sensible criticisms, many difficulties, nothing could deflect him from this loyalty now. He therefore became deeply involved, at the age of sixty-one, in a wholly new enterprise.

Appendix to Chapter III

Dates in William Tuke's Life

1732	Born in York. Largely cared for by aunt and uncle, Mary and Henry Frankland.
1740	Henry Frankland died.
1746	Apprenticed to Mary Frankland.
1748	His father died.
1752	Mary Frankland died. William inherited her business.
1754	Married Elizabeth Hoyland.
1755	His mother died.
	His son Henry born; there followed four other children, Sarah, William, John, Elizabeth.
1760	His wife Elizabeth died giving birth to the youngest child, Elizabeth.
1765	Married Esther Maud. They had three children of whom Ann and Mabel survived.
1770	William's son Henry, aged 15, apprenticed to the tea business.
1779	Ackworth School founded.
1781	Henry married Mary Maria Scott.
1783	William Tuke Clerk to Yearly Meeting.
1784	Samuel Tuke, William's grandson, born.
1785	Henry became a partner in the business.
	Esther and William started a girls' school in Trinity Lane.
1790	Hannah Mills died at York Asylum.
1792	William Tuke started the idea of The Retreat.
1794	Esther Tuke died after a long illness.
1796	Samuel Tuke apprenticed to the tea business.
	May: The Retreat opened with three patients.
	July: Timothy Maud died and William Tuke had to undertake to manage the Retreat. Dr. Fowler became visiting physician.
	September: Katherine Allen came to be Senior Nurse.
1797	George Jepson became superintendent.

1802   Dr. Fowler died, succeeded by Dr. Cappe and then Dr. Belcombe.

1805   Samuel Tuke became a partner in the business.

1806   George Jepson and Katherine Allen married.

1812   Esther Tuke's school given up. (The Mount was founded in 1831.)

1813   Descripton of The Retreat by Samuel Tuke published. Reviewed immediately by Sydney Smith in the Edinburgh Review.

1814   Henry Tuke died.

1815/6   Select Committee of the House of Commons on Madhouses. (Legislation on this did not follow till 1828.)

1818   William Tuke retired from the tea business.

1821   The Jepsons retired from The Retreat

1822   William Tuke died.

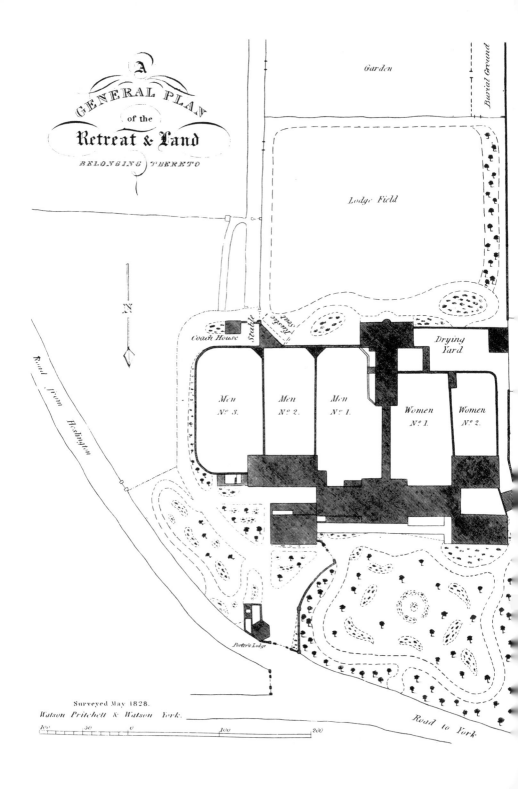

A
GENERAL PLAN
of the
Retreat & Land
BELONGING THERETO

Garden

Burial Ground

Lodge Field

N.

Coach House

Stable

Stable

Drying
Yard

Road from Heslington

Men
Nᵒ 3.

Men
Nᵒ 2.

Men
Nᵒ 1.

Women
Nᵒ 1.

Women
Nᵒ 2.

Porter's Lodge

Surveyed May 1828.
Watson Pritchett & Watson York.

100   50   0   100   200

Road to York.

CHAPTER IV

Beginnings

THE Retreat had a difficult start. To begin with there was very inadequate support from the Society of Friends. 'After mature reflection and several consultations with his most intimate friends', especially Lindley Murray, of *English Grammar* fame, William Tuke decided to put his suggestion before the March Quarterly Meeting in 1792. This Meeting was not actually held in March, because a public execution was announced for the chosen date, so it was held in April. There are no Minutes of this discussion; Tuke must have had his say when the formal meeting was over. Daniel Hack Tuke, William's great-grandson, summed it all up years later in the words 'A wet blanket was thrown upon the scheme'. He describes his great-grandfather's style in argument as *fortiter in re*, forceful and to the point; he says people did not like it. The debate went against Tuke and the project was obviously going to be dropped when Henry Tuke said: 'But is there nothing to be said for my father's idea?' and the discussion began again. Henry's manner in argument is described as *suaviter in modo*, pleasant and persuasive, and he carried the day. William Tuke was instructed to draw up a detailed plan of what he wanted to do.

A series of brochures and appeals followed, addressed to the Society at large. Tuke never seems to have made a claim that Quakers would run their asylum *better* than others; and Samuel Tuke believed that at that date his grandfather knew little about the general situation and how very bad it was. Indeed, nobody knew much until after the publication of the Reports of the Select Committee of the House of Commons on Madhouses in 1815/6. Tuke based his appeals on the consideration that it would be better for Quakers to be looked after in mental illness, and still more in convalescence, by Quakers.

However, this religious argument did not cut much ice, and Friends found plenty of reasons for withholding support. They probably assumed that all that could be done for these unhappy people was already being done; that if visitors were excluded from asylums, this was in the best interests of the patients, and any hardships or privations were unavoidable, although they were shaken by the case of Hannah Mills. It was not supposed that there were in fact many Friends in need of such provision, and York Friends did not fancy the concentration of mentally-ill patients in their neighbourhood. When Tuke presented a scheme for a house to hold thirty patients, he was told that this was too large for the catchment area of Yorkshire and the adjoining counties; and if he was thinking of a national institution, London was the place for it, and he should refer his proposal to Yearly Meeting: if he had a concern for the insane in Yorkshire, a contribution to the York Asylum was the obvious answer. It was misgivings about the York Asylum that first prompted his suggestion, but he did not wish to say so.

By June 1795 funds had accumulated only very modestly indeed. William at this difficult time was much encouraged by the enthusiasm shown by his friend, Lindley Murray. Murray was a devoted Friend, also a man of great charm, and chair-bound invalid though he was, he became deeply interested in The Retreat. Some of the drafts of the Rules are in his handwriting, and he applied his mind also to the problems of finance. He encouraged the idea of annuities, a method of giving which appealed to a number of Friends. These were promises of annuities (on which interest of 5% was paid to the annuitants) amounting to £325; donations of £799.13.6; annual subscriptions of £32.0.6. At this point a decision was taken by a meeting of 'the friends of the institution' to go ahead.

That the 'institution' should be named *The Retreat* was the inspired suggestion of Mary. Maria, Henry Tuke's wife. A plan was now approved:

> 'that ground be purchased and a building erected to accommodate Thirty Patients, in an airy situation, and at as short a distance from York as possible, so as to have the privilege of retirement; and that there be a few acres for keeping cows and for garden ground for the family; which will afford some scope for the Patients to take exercise.'

'The family' did not mean Tuke's family, who never lived at The Retreat; the word always means the community consisting of Superintendent, nursing and domestic staff, and patients. The word illuminates what Daniel Hack Tuke called the 'homeishness' of the house.

At the end of 1793 they thought they were lucky to get the site where The Retreat still stands. 'Its distance was only half a mile from the city, the ground was elevated, and the situation affords excellent air and water, as well as an extensive and diversified prospect.' They bought twenty acres for £2,325 and at once sold eight acres for £968. They engaged the services of a London architect, John Bevans, who designed a building at a cost of £1,883.4.1. There were those who thought, and said, that it should have been possible to rent a house in York, at least to start with, much more cheaply, and that if The Retreat were not a success, a purpose-built house of this size would be harder to sell than an ordinary house.

The architect (who in the event did not take a fee), planned the building to meet William Tuke's ideas of what was needed. These were imaginative, original and lavish; the architecture of compassion, quite unlike most asylums. Comfort for the patient was the governing idea, and was built into the house from the bottom up. An outstanding feature is the long wide corridors, or galleries as they called them; these were to enable restless patients to walk up and down, even if they were not fit to go out, and patients do that to this day. If they are prevented from moving, they are liable to become aggressive. The windows of The Retreat have small panes reinforced by invisible iron bars so that while it would not be possible to commit suicide by throwing oneself out, the house does not in the least look like a prison. The floors are of wood, not stone. Tuke had been advised that mad people sometimes fight, and that a fall on to a wooden floor is less likely to cause injury than crashing on to stone. Some of the timber was imported from America.

At the beginning of 1795 'the building was covered in and the inside work in great forwardness; but the funds being entirely expended it was agreed at a meeting of subscribers to borrow what might be necessary to complete the place for the reception of patients'. The build-up of funds from fees could not begin till patients had actually arrived.

John Hipsley (sometimes spelt Hippisley), the husband of Tuke's daughter Mabel, gave a lot of help in connection with the building and for this purpose lived in York for some months; but it would seem that characteristically William Tuke himself carried major responsibility; there are quantities of receipts made out to him for building material, wood, stone, brick and tiles, all of good quality. One forms the impression that the quantity surveying must have been amateurish, but Tuke was working with a very narrow margin of money, and sent for materials in small quantities as and when the workmen needed them.

While the building was going up Tuke ordered three hundred trees, some of which, including the great beeches along the wall by the York Road, he planted himself. A friend gave expert help in choosing a cow, but she turned out a bad buy and had to be replaced. Tuke bought beds for all; no one, not even the incontinent, was going to sleep on straw. He also bought spoons; many inmates of lunatic asylums had to eat with their fingers, but not the Quakers at The Retreat.

Between the years 1792 and 1795, while William was becoming so deeply involved in his new scheme, he and his family suffered personal tragedy. Esther became ill in 1792. Her exhaustion must have had something to do with that much-quoted remark of hers, made in

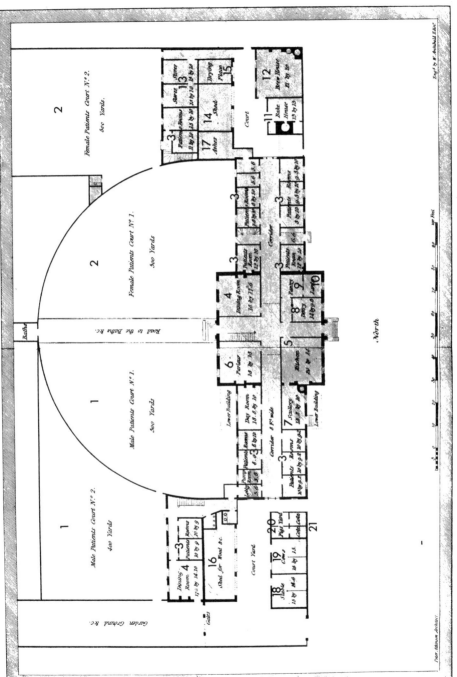

GROUND PLAN of the RETREAT near YORK.

Taken from Samuel Tuke's Description of The Retreat 1813

Key to Plan

1 Male Patients' Courts
2 Female Patients' Courts
3 Patients Rooms
4 Dining Room
5 Kitchen
6 Parlour
7 Scullery
8 Dairy
9 Pantry
10 Larder
11 Bake House

12 Brew House
13 Stores
14 Shed
15 Drying Place
16 Shed for Wood
17 Ashes
18 Stable
19 Cows
20 Pigs Yard
21 Cote

33

response to William's enthusiasm for founding The Retreat — 'Thee has many wonderful children of thy brain, dear William, but this is surely an idiot birth'. Poor Esther became housebound and realised that all her wonderful energy was ebbing away. She died on February 13th, 1794, aged 68. For many years she had been the guiding influence in her family and a leading figure in the Society of Friends, and since 1785 the head mistress at the school. There seem to be no extant written records from William's pen about his reaction to the loss of his second wife, but it must have hit him very hard. Although he was immensely helped by the loving devotion of his son Henry and of Mary Maria, he had to face this bereavement, and all the re-adjustments one has to make when such losses come upon a family, at the very time when he was exerting himself to the full in the initial affairs of The Retreat.

The building went forward very well, and in 1795 a constitution was drawn up for the Management of The Retreat. It was to be governed by a meeting of subscribers held quarterly. There was to be a monthly visitation by two Friends appointed *ad hoc* by the York Meeting, who were to sign their names on each occasion in a book kept for the purpose and enter any comments that occurred to them. William Tuke was determined that there should be no exclusion of the public, with the possibility of secret scandals developing as at York Asylum: The Retreat was to be continuously and deliberately exposed to the inspection and comment of independent observers. The day to day business was to be in the hands of a small executive committee, meeting weekly. This committee at first consisted of Thomas Priestman, Timothy White, John Fothergill, William Tuke himself and his son John. The first Minutes of this Executive are recorded for January 1st, 1796.

There were a number of immediate tasks for this committee, especially the settlement of the fees to be charged, and the appointment of staff. The usual fee for patients at institutions for the insane was twelve to fifteen shillings a week; this was for places offering far less comfort than The Retreat. When Mary Lamb's recurrent illness obliged her to go into a Home, Charles paid for her at the rate of £60 per year. The Retreat settled on eight shillings a week as the usual fee, but were prepared to accept four shillings a week for poor Quakers, who were vouched for by their own Meeting as in need, and for whom their own Meeting could not help to pay. At the other end of the scale, The Retreat could offer more comfort and a private room for fees of up to one pound a week. A personal servant or relative could accompany a patient and be accommodated for six shillings a week. Such assistants were often invaluable. Hannah Ponsonby, who came under this arrangement to look after her mother in 1797, eventually joined the staff and in 1822 succeeded to the office of matron. Fees were always discussed and agreed with the families of patients, and if their circumstances changed, and a reduction was asked for, the Committee seem always to have agreed.

Some light on the cost of food is found in a letter of Charles Lamb to a friend, when his sister Mary wrote to decline an invitation to dinner, and the friend had to pay 2d. on the letter: in those days the postage was paid by the recipient. 'If Mary comes she will eat beef, two plates 4d., batter pudding, one plate 2d., wine three glasses (I drink no wine) 11d., tea and supper at moderate calculation 9d., walnuts 2d., total two shillings and six pence, from which deduct postage 2d., you are a clear gainer by her not coming.' An early chemist's bill, receipted to George Jepson, the first Superintendent, lists small quantities of sal volatile, sulphate of ammonia, sulphate of magnesia, tincture digitalis and colchicum, camphor, castor oil, linseed oil, cinnamon, rhubarb, lavender water, peppermint water, spirit of turpentine, restringent powders, croton oil, cardomums, and tartar emetic. If only more such receipts had been kept, we could have had some idea of the ordinary remedies used. It is clear that the very low fees charged could not possibly have covered the costs of food, however minimal these seem to us, or the costs of prescriptions, even those based on very simple ingredients.

The problem of finding staff was not easy. William Tuke was aware of the crucial importance of the quality of the staff and anxious about it. He hoped to find someone of his own class to be Superintendent, and had his eye on John Hipsley, the father of the John Hipsley who was his son-in-law; he meant to engage men and women of the type of 'good upper servants' to form the assistant staff. It is not clear to what extent, if at all, Tuke felt it necessary to seek attendants who had had experience with the mentally ill. He wanted men and women who were Quakers, and were kind and reliable. There is no suggestion that John Hipsley had any relevant experience; he had been a successful headmaster at Ackworth School from 1791 to 1795. The first staff appointment was Joshua Cardingley, who arrived in April 1796; he was 'accustomed to the care of patients disordered in their minds' and was to be paid £15.15s a year. On May 11th Jane King came to be housekeeper, while her wages were still under discussion, and 'the Family commenced house-keeping on this day'.

However, during May, John Hipsley announced his intention of leaving York. This must have been disconcerting, but Tuke at once approached his brother-in-law, Timothy Maud, and he agreed to accept the post. He was retiring from a medical practice in Bradford, and is described as a surgeon and also an apothecary; a warm-hearted man. It would obviously have been an advantage to The Retreat to have a medical man as Superintendent.

Also in May, Ann Retton came to take charge of women patients: we have no record of what her qualifications may have been. She was followed by a cook, a chambermaid, a man servant and a woman servant. They were all to give help with patients, as might be needed, as well as doing their special jobs. Thus The Retreat had a ratio of seven staff to a planned total of thirty patients, a higher proportion than was usual. It should be noted that Ann Retton and Joshua Cardingley were expected to sleep near their patients, to be available at night if necessary, a most onerous arrangement. Dr. Conolly wrote many years later about the difficulties in an asylum at night. He described how a patient could be tolerably tranquil by day, but 'with the night, restless distraction comes . . . the attendant who has fastened down his troublesome and sleepless patients in bed, retires with a satisfied mind to his supper and his rest. Patients may suffer from heat and thirst and may yell and shout in their despair'. Conolly said that at Hanwell, when the attendant heard a banging on the inside of the patient's locked door, he would go along and 'give him water or a hot drink . . . make his bed comfortable again, bathe his hands and face, give him some tobacco'. But Conolly noted that not all attendants were as good as that, and some would give the disturbing patient rough treatment. Tuke does not describe such night nursing at The Retreat but it must have been needed.

Tuke's first appointments did not turn out to be very satisfactory. Joshua Cardingley was not a good mental nurse; he could not keep the men patients 'quiet and still', he absented himself without leave, and during his absence his patients appeared to get on better than when he was there. These criticisms come from a contemporary letter of William Tuke. Jane King was not up to her job, which she found a great strain; there was a not unexpected death of a patient, and poor Jane 'let down her spirits' when she should have been setting an example of steadiness; within a year she wished to leave and The Retreat was glad to let her go. Ann Retton was not a Quaker and this was regretted, because one of the main reasons for setting up The Retreat was to provide Quaker nursing for Quaker patients. It was planned to replace her as soon as they could find a Quaker girl to take responsibility for women patients. In contrast Hannah Hall, the humblest of women servants, turned out to be worth her weight in gold.

The first patients arrived in June, 1796. They were Mrs. Mary Holt, 'sometimes low and melancholy' but 'mostly active and talkative';

Mrs. Rachel Row, who had been 'deranged for two years, her ideas very wild' who saw figures in clouds and fire, and heard voices; and a mould-maker from Coalbrookdale, a single man called John Ellis, described as 'maniacal'.

As the summer wore on, more patients came, some from very long distances: within a year or so they had come from Yorkshire, the North, the Midlands, Bristol, Gloucester, Penzance. The difficulty of making these long horse-drawn journeys, which involved putting up for at least one night on the way, and in some cases for more than one, must have been most daunting and indeed hazardous for the people who brought in these patients. They all arrived exhausted and dispirited.

The Minutes of the Committee for June 13th, 1796, records that 'a Physician being necessary as Patients are now coming', Dr. Thomas Fowler was offered and accepted an appointment as visiting physician. He and the Committee agreed that he should serve them for a year without remuneration, and then discuss the matter, as neither he nor they could foretell how much work would be involved for him. At the end of the year it was arranged through a third party, for William Tuke loathed discussing salaries directly, so he said, that £25 would be right.

Fowler had worked in his youth in a chemist's shop in York; he took the degree of M.D. in Edinburgh, and started to practice in Stafford. At the Infirmary there, he and the apothecary compounded a remedy for ague, which remained in use till well into the 20th century: it is an arsenical medicine, known as Fowler's Solution. He was the author of several books, the best known of which dealt with the effects of tobacco, and another with the use of arsenic, in the treatment among other ailments of 'periodic headaches'. His work in Stafford came to an end when he had a cardiac breakdown. On his recovery, he returned to York in 1793.

His appointment at The Retreat gave offence in York. He had little experience in the field of insanity, and a doctor who had a reputation for treating this type of illness was passed over. This was the visiting physician of York Asylum, who offered his services. One can imagine he would be the last man whom Tuke would wish to see assuming responsibility at The Retreat. Apart from Tuke's profound distrust of the York Asylum, he would want to have his own way in a number of matters; and Fowler was an inexperienced and also a modest man. Fowler had another quality that would appeal to Tuke, an uncommonly open mind. He had, besides, an experimental, scientific approach to medical problems which was of very great benefit to The Retreat. Samuel Tuke, who may have known him, says he was 'a man equally distinguished by medical knowledge and indefatigable perseverance . . . a highly benevolent and unprejudiced mind . . . He entered upon his office with the anxiety and ardour of a feeling mind, upon the extent of whose skill depended the dearest interests of many of his fellow creatures'.

In July of this same year, 1796, a major blow fell upon The Retreat. Timothy Maud died after only two months' service. When John Hipsley had said he was leaving York, Tuke knew exactly what to do and at once turned to Maud. Now he and the Committee were completely at a loss. William Tuke offered 'to attend by day for a week' and this offer was accepted. It had been no part of his original intention to run The Retreat himself, and he had to go on doing it for about a year. He badly missed his wife and his brother-in-law.

'To attend by day' might mean a brief daily visit; but a letter of 1st December, 1796 shows us Tuke giving careful attention to the details of the management of individual patients, and closely watching their condition from day to day. This unquestionably meant considerable neglect of his business.

He was now working actively in a field in which he had no experience and in which his physician had very little. He had done some reading about insanity, since 1792 when he determined to found The Retreat, and he had visited some asylums, but clearly he had much to learn.

Tuke had two *a priori* notions of his own about the treatment of the insane. The first was that they need as much physical comfort as possible. Tuke thought they should be clothed, as many lunatics were not; fed, although many lunatics were starved to reduce their strength; clean; and treated with kind civility instead of vituperation. The meals at The Retreat were good and ample, with meat at least five times a week, fruit twice, and a lot of milk from their own cows. One man who arrived starved had a huge appetite; he was encouraged to take as much as he wanted until he had assuaged his accumulated hunger. Samuel Tuke says that some patients, especially convalescents, positively need snacks of wine and biscuits between meals. Most of us find that our sense of security in a strange environment is steadied when we realise that the food is good. But Tuke's thoughts went beyond these basic provisions to what De La Rive, a Swiss doctor who visited The Retreat in 1798, called *les douceurs de la vie*: tea, coffee, beer, wine, space, gardens, trees and more. The notion that comfort is a factor in mental therapy is interesting. It was quite out of keeping with the standards in the care of the insane that were common at the time.

People at The Retreat would find their sense of security confirmed by contact with William Tuke. He is described as being 'about average height, with a noble forehead and an eagle eye'. With his valuable endowment of self-will, Tuke was naturally dominating. There is no suggestion, in the letters and records that survive, that he had difficulty in controlling patients, or that he expected any. They would find security in his confidence, and also in his kindness. When he died a patient wrote a poem about him which contained the lines:

What tenderness with strength combined
Dwelt in his energetic mind.

This is not great poetry, but it is a precise statement of fact.

William Tuke's second preconceived idea about the management of the insane was that they should be kept 'quiet and still'. This too was a highly original notion and many would have thought it quite impractical. Most asylums seem to have been full of noise, if not turbulence, most of the time, some patients 'vociferous', Samuel Tuke's favourite word for a patient on the verge of becoming violent, others protesting loudly against restraint and vituperating attendants and other patients. As a Quaker and by temperament, William Tuke was well qualified to instil calm; but Joseph Cardingley was not, a fact which William Tuke noted uneasily in a letter of 1796. Cardingley, who had had experience of handling insane patients, had probably got it in some place where the normal methods of intimidation and the use of force were taught as necessary skills. Moreover Dr. Fowler at this time was conscientiously prescribing the usual horrible medical treatments, which must have created periodic protest and disturbance. Nevertheless Tuke won. Dr. De la Rive in 1798, among other very early visitors, was impressed by the surprising quietness of The Retreat.

Patients continued to arrive; by September 1796 there were eight. In that month a most fortunate event occurred. A Quaker girl was found to replace Ann Retton, who was given a month's wages and left almost at once. The new nurse was Katherine Allen. She had had good experience at a Quaker 'insanarium' in Somerset under Dr. Fox. The Retreat got written testimonials for her, some of which have survived. One came from Dr. Fox's brother: 'K. Allen is a smart Friend' (i.e. did not at that time wear Quaker dress), 'stout . . . and professes an inclination for undertaking ye care of insane patients . . . She seems to have much good humour and she appears to me to be such a one as I should like to commend an insane friend to. She always sat at table with those Patients at my brother's who walked the house. She was employed by Dr. E. F. in fetching patients from their homes and appears to have resolution'. She must have needed resolution to face those journeys in such company. E. Hipsley also knew something of her and wrote: 'She is an agreeable young woman and was thought very clever at her place at Dr. Fox's. She was thought very good-natured which I think is a very good thing in a nurse'. She had left Dr. Fox because of some illness, but

A SKETCH

ORIGIN,

PROGRESS, AND PRESENT STATE

OF

THE RETREAT,

AN INSTITUTION NEAR YORK,

FOR THE RECEPTION OF PERSONS AFFLICTED

WITH

DISORDERS OF THE MIND,

AMONG THE SOCIETY OF FRIENDS.

———

DRAWN UP BY DIRECTION OF THE

GENERAL MEETING,

FOR

Distribution among the Subscribers.

———

PRINTED BY W. ALEXANDER AND SON, CASTLEGATE.

1828.

this did not deter The Retreat from engaging her, and apparently it never recurred. She was a very striking personality, and her appointment brought great benefit to The Retreat.

Dr. Fox, under whom she worked, was a Quaker and his insanarium was very good indeed. When Katherine was on his staff he had a small house at Cleve Hill at Downend at Bristol. It was in 1806 that he moved to a larger place at Brislington. This institution is described with much praise by W. L. Parry-Jones. Dr. Fox was one of the first proprietors of licensed houses to manage patients humanely and without restraint. The house and grounds were ample, and the house was well-heated. He provided occupation, recreation and exercise; some women had silver pheasants and doves in their courtyard, and greyhounds were kept for their amusement. The story of Cowper's pleasure, during his mental illness, in a tame hare, and how the villagers brought him several more, since they understood the poor gentleman liked hares, illustrates the fact that the companionship, or at least company, of animals may minister in some way to some insane persons. Dr. Fox wished his patients to have a life that approximated as far as possible to ordinary social life, and therefore he paid a clergyman to conduct Anglican services at his asylum, in spite of being a Quaker himself. The full developments at Brislington were going on at the same time as the start of The Retreat. But it is natural to assume that Katherine Allen had learnt much at Cleve Hill. Many of the features of Dr. Fox's establishment are found in the story of The Retreat.

At The Retreat Katherine quickly won the confidence of William Tuke, and as she seems to have been both cheerful and also bossy, she probably taught many of the staff a great deal. She 'had resolution', and she was a positive, creative person. When she arrived to be principal nurse to the female patients, it was arranged for her to sit at the Housekeeper's table, or that of the Superintendent, and to be regarded as 'an Officer rather than a servant'. A year later when Jane King departed, she was promoted to Housekeeper, the senior post for women, retaining a general responsibility for the care of women patients.

We have two pictures of life at The Retreat during the year when Tuke was running it himself. One rather late account is from the *Sketch of The Retreat*, drawn up by the direction of General Meeting for distribution among the subscribers in 1828:

The original promoters of the establishment, whilst sensible that great abuses existed in many houses devoted to the care of the insane . . . imagined also that there were others from whose practice they might derive the results of an enlightened experience;

41

and by whose precepts they might safely in great measure be guided in the main principles of their moral and medical treatment. The basis of the system at that time generally adopted was the position that fear is the great principle by which the insane are to be governed; and the principle consequences deduced from it were that their attendants should commence their intercourse with (patients) by an appearance of austerity, and perhaps the display of physical prowess; in fact that in some cases of violent excitement the cudgel and the whip were the most suitable instruments of coercion. We believe it may be said that The Retreat commenced with an assent to the general correctness of these views; and although they could not fail to be modified by the good sense and feeling of the committee of management, it must be admitted that they were acted upon to an extent which with our present knowledge we can hardly contemplate without surprise.

This picture is so out of keeping with the general impression that everybody had and has of Tuke, that we cannot help raising the question whether it is to be believed. One question of importance is, who helped to write *The Sketch*? It is sometimes attributed to Samuel Tuke. But Samuel Tuke virtually contradicted it in a later signed writing; and moreover at the time to which these paragraphs apply he was either away at school or kept, one supposes, very busy, as the new apprentice in the shop at the other end of York. These paragraphs are written with assurance, suggesting first-hand knowledge; the only person one can name as possibly one of the authors of *The Sketch* who could speak with personal knowledge of the early months of The Retreat is John Tuke, son of William, a member of the original weekly committee. He was the only member of that committee who was still living in 1828.

An earlier and much more intimate picture of life at The Retreat at this time comes from William Tuke's letter of 1st December, 1796. It illustrates vividly his irritation with Jane King and her lack of good judgment, his confidence in Katherine Allen; but over and above that, his earnest care for patients and his sense of being almost overwhelmed with the difficulties at The Retreat, when the institution was afflicted with a lot of illness.

Jane King, though unwell herself, in imprudent officiousness would, against Katherine's advice, sit up with E. Thompson in the early stages of the disorder, and thus became very nearly as ill herself, and was probably making it worse by not making it known at the proper time to the doctor. She has now been near a week confined to her bed. The cook also has been so ill of a strong feverish cold that the doctor has thought it necessary for her to keep her bed for a day or two, and the new assistant to the nurses has had a bad whitlow, so as to render her unwell and one hand disabled. Thus thou wilt see that the Family has been greatly deranged indeed. However there is a better side to look at. John Ellis has for some weeks been getting more quiet and still since Joshua left'. (Joshua Cardingley had been away on some business and did not return when expected. John Ellis was the maniacal mould-maker from Coalbrookedale.) 'I have also every day observed an improvement. He is now so well as to sit with other Patients without the Jacket and with common clothes and though attended with some complaint in the bowels for a few days keeps himself clean, and in every respect conducts himself as a person in his right mind. Mary Evans has also today manifested an inclination for a particular sort of tea-cake, I am not sure whether we understand her meaning, but I have sent up such as I supposed she wanted. It is very extraordinary that she should enquire for anything to eat; she also manifested some other symptoms yesterday and today which I think favourable, and if those two should be restored to their right minds, the institution will get some credit.

During this time when so many of the staff were unwell, Hannah Hall made herself exceptionally useful, and this was not forgotten. Some months later when salaries were being considered, she got a rise and a present of a guinea in recognition of her services at a time when 'extraordinary assistance and labour were necessary'. But very shortly after William Tuke wrote this letter expressing some optimism about John Ellis, another blow fell. Ellis's condition deteriorated sharply about a week before it was planned for him to go home. Joshua Cardingley, who was responsible for him, noticed this but failed to reflect that since he was worse and more melancholic, he ought to have the door of his room locked at night, as it had been earlier on in his illness. On the night of January 9th, or early the next morning, he left his room. Cardingley did not hear him moving and Ellis contrived to hang himself. This was, of course, a terrible blow. Tuke instantly sacked Joshua Cardingley on the grounds of negligence. Cardingley's departure probably helped The Retreat a good deal; it is impossible to think William Tuke had ever brandished 'the whip and the cudgel'; if anyone at The Retreat really did this, it might be that Cardingley did. In fact it may have been this that made it difficult for him to keep the men patients quiet and still, and made them noticeably more peaceful when he was away.

Tuke got a man called Samuel Tottie to come in Joshua's place. He arranged for him to come after Joshua had gone so that the two men did

Taken from *A Sketch of the Origin, Progress & Present State of The Retreat* drawn up by General Meeting, 1828

Key to Plan

1.	Male Patients' Court	11.	Pantry
2.	Men's Day Room	11a.	Larder
3.	Female Patients' Court	12.	Scullery
4.	Women's Day Room	13.	Knife Room
5.	Patients' Rooms	14.	Parlour
5a.	Bedrooms	15.	Refectory
6.	Superintendent's Office	16.	Servants
7.	Apothecarie's Office	17.	Dressing Room
8.	Reading Room	18.	Wash House
9.	Dining Room	19.	Hot Bath
10.	Kitchen	19a.	Hot Closet
10a.	Back Kitchen	20.	Cold Bath
10b.	Bake House		

21.	Laundry
22.	Drying Yard
23.	Straw
24.	Coals
25.	Ashes
26.	Stable
27.	Brew House
28.	Dead Room
29.	Stores
30.	Work Room
31.	Warehouse
32.	Coach House

45

not meet. Tottie was not an ideal appointment; he was not a Quaker, and moreover he was wanting to get married, so that a job that entailed night duty could not suit him for long. But he was a good nurse, he took it for granted that he slept near his patients at night and they found him acceptable. After he had gone, he was sometimes asked to come back for a time to act as personal servant to a man patient.

Thus at the beginning of 1797 The Retreat urgently needed both a Superintendent to relieve William Tuke, and also a keeper for the men patients so that Samuel Tottie could leave to get married. Tuke asked John Hipsley whether he would consider returning to York to take charge at The Retreat, but Hipsley refused.

Tuke wrote William Maud about this difficulty; they had discussed a man called George Jepson as a possible keeper. He was a self-employed weaver at Knaresborough, an unmarried man of 53 and an active Friend who would have been known to Tuke through Quarterly Meeting. In addition to his weaving he practised as a self-taught apothecary. (It was not until 1813 that it became illegal to do this without a written qualification and a long apprenticeship.) People came to consult Jepson from far and wide, not only about their illnesses, but also about their private concerns. It was part of the profession of the apothecary to act not only as medical adviser but also as counsellor. Tuke thought on reflection that 'George Jepson's talents were above those of a keeper'. Also he began to feel that he had aimed too high, when he planned to get someone of his own class to superintend at The Retreat, and he asked Maud whether they could, in fact, find a better Superintendent than Jepson. 'Had he been more experienced in the government and order of a pretty large family, I should not have much doubt respecting him. I consider him as a steady, religious Friend and in that respect to be fully confided in. His knowledge of medicine would be of great use to the institution, and his qualifications in writing, and (I hope), with instruction, to keep the accounts in the proper method.'

William Tuke felt far from confident in proposing this. He suggested to Jepson that he should come to The Retreat for a week, to help him with some Minutes, without letting anyone at Knaresborough or York know that anything further was in the wind; this would give the Committee a chance to form an opinion of Jepson, and Tuke did not wish to influence them on this matter; and also it would give Jepson the opportunity to consider whether The Retreat seemed to him to offer the kind of work for which he should give up his independent business and his patients. He was an extremely modest man, and this may have helped to make Tuke uncertain about appointing him to a position in which he ought to exercise authority.

The Committee made up their minds about Jepson more quickly than he did about them. When invited to become Superintendent, he wished to come for three months without commitment on either side. Tuke wrote in a letter of February 13th, 1797, 'G. J. said he thought of spending a little more time at The Retreat previous to his coming to a conclusion. His coming at present would be particularly acceptable'. In the end he accepted a permanent appointment in the spring of 1797.

This appointment was to prove far more important than Tuke or Jepson or anyone else realised. Tuke had thought that he would be useful in several ways: with the accounts, and as an apothecary, and as the general Superintendent of the Family. George did keep the weekly accounts; there are innumerable small weekly receipts made out to him. But it seems unlikely that accounts were ever a strong point of his. There came a day when he could not tell whether or not he had spent three shillings and six pence at Bradford, where he had gone to fetch back a run-away patient. 'I tell George', said William, 'that the Tukes have bad memories but his is worse'. Dr. Daniel Hack Tuke, writing in 1880, says Jepson's medical knowledge was not important (this is a doctor commenting on an apothecary), and that 'he was at first too much addicted to the lancet'. Daniel Hack Tuke adds, with insight, that his value to The Retreat lay largely in his freedom from the conditioning of the mind which an ordinary medical training would have induced.

What Tuke did not expect was that Jepson would turn out to have exceptional gifts in dealing with mental patients. Had Knaresborough been nearer to York, Tuke might have known some of Jepson's patients there, and seen how valuable he would be as a mental nurse. But without this knowledge Tuke was not confident that he had got what it would take to manage The Retreat, and Jepson had even less confidence. We do not know what considerations led him to give up his long practice at Knaresborough, where he was much trusted, for work in an asylum to which he was entirely new. We may presume that after deep consideration, it seemed to him that there was, as some would say, 'a call' for him at The Retreat and so he knew that The Retreat was where he must be. His decision brought incalculable benefit to The Retreat, to its patients and to its staff, and William Tuke quickly came to realise his qualities. Samuel Tuke later recorded that George Jepson had 'carried into effect the benevolent wishes of the original promoters . . . beyond their most sanguine expectations'.

So an asylum for mental patients was now being run by a tea-merchant, a physician and a weaver, none of whom had any qualifications for the job.

In June, 1797, the Committee submitted the First Annual Report to the General Meeting. In this they mentioned several points that added up to encouragement. First and foremost they had been fully confirmed in their belief that The Retreat was needed. Patients came to them sometimes from great distances, sometimes from their own homes, where they had often been unskilfully cared for; sometimes from asylums where conditions were very bad, so that they got worse instead of better. They did not know of Quakers being penalised for being Quakers, but they put very well the religious argument for a Quaker institution: 'There has been particular occasion to observe the great loss which individuals in our Society have sustained, by being put under the care of those who are not only strangers to our principles; but by whom they are frequently mixed with other patients who may indulge themselves in ill language and other exceptional practices. This often seems to have an unprofitable effect upon the patients' minds, alienating those religious attachments which they had before experienced, and sometimes even corrupting them with vicious habits, to which they had been strangers'.

They were confident that patients at The Retreat had improved after coming there. 'Eighteen have been admitted, most of whom from the long continuance of their disorder may be deemed incurables. Two patients have died, one is gone home recovered, and several others are greatly improved; and though the symptoms of derangement in these may still be obvious, yet they appear in general more easy and comfortable than under such circumstances might be expected.' The Retreat people were sensitive to their own lack of experience, but were confident that patients were not suffering from this. What they had set their hearts on was not cure, a word they never use; but that deranged Quakers might have their illness in peace and comfort, and if possible improve in general health.

They report that the staff is adequate; they have a Physician; 'a man Friend, well approved, hath undertaken the office of superintendent, and a woman Friend that of housekeeper. These, with two men and three women servants form the present establishment of the house'. There were fifteen patients. They report that they are impressed with the value of occupation, or attendance at religious meetings, and of the regular visits of women Friends from York.

In speaking of finance, they refer to 'the great debt with which the Institution is encumbered', and hope that subscriptions and legacies may be forthcoming. Of the fifteen patients then in the house, seven were paying only four shillings a week, the rest from eight shillings to one guinea, and the total income per week was six pounds five shillings. They hope that when they have more patients they will cover the weekly outlay from the weekly fees. 'The terms are lower than those of any Institution of the kind which we know of.'

General Meeting was content to leave the fees as they were. It was agreed to raise a loan to pay off the bills for the building, which amounted to £1,300; in this they met with no difficulty, £600 was forthcoming at once and the remainder not long after. The arduous and indeed hazardous experiment had survived its first year in good order. But many problems were unsolved.

William's wife, Esther, had always felt more anxiety about financial risk than he did. She also had a fine sense of the probable, and seems to have believed that The Retreat would not have much appeal for most Quakers: and if this is what she thought, she was quite right, at least so far as the early years were concerned. Had she lived to see how The Retreat managed its finances, her anxieties would have multiplied.

To recapitulate:

(i)   There was no rich benefactor to underwrite the enterprise. They were entirely dependent on subscriptions and donations and on patients' fees. The Retreat was constantly in debt to William Tuke to the extent of hundreds of pounds and for lesser sums to the Superintendent.

(ii)   Subscriptions and donations at first brought in very little indeed; it seemed that the Society was unlikely to back the scheme.

(iii)   They charged unusually low fees. William Tuke told a friend in a letter in 1796 that he had learned that the normal fee for patients at asylums was fifteen shillings a week. He and the Committee of Management decided to charge eight shillings as the regular fee, but to accept patients at four shillings a week if they were too poor to pay more, were vouched for by their Meeting, and if the Meeting concerned could not help them.

(iv)   A year later they agreed to accept such poor Quakers for a year for nothing, provided they sought admission within six months of the onset of their illness. This was because their brief experience had already persuaded them that patients' best chance of recovery depended on early hospitalisation.

(v)   Their expenditure was lavish from the very beginning; a large estate, a large purpose-built house, lavish amenities, *les douceurs de la vie*, plenty of food. Elizabeth Gurney, later Mrs. Fry, and her father 'thought it extravagantly carried on'.

(vi)   They borrowed £1,300 before the building was complete, and in their first annual report expressed their anxiety about 'the great debt with which the Institution is encumbered . . . it is hoped that subscriptions and legacies will come in so as not only to pay the interest . . . but also gradually to reduce it'. But long before they had paid off this debt, they added to their indebtedness by adding to their buildings again and again and again; in fact in 1796, 1798, 1803 and 1809.

This seems a very odd way for Quaker men of business to handle a novel and experimental enterprise, undertaken in fact against the judgment of many sensible people. How is it to be understood?

The initial decision to go ahead on very scanty funds, contributed and promised, must, one supposes, have been influenced by the earlier experiences with Ackworth School, with which William Tuke had been much identified. There too there had been very little interest when the foundation of a school was proposed, even at York Meeting, only thirty miles away; but ample support was accorded when it started. On the other hand it was perhaps natural that many Quakers would be glad to send their children to a Quaker school, but few would think of a lunatic asylum as a project that concerned them at all nearly.

The high expenditure on physical comfort is particularly surprising; it was un-Quakerly according to the teaching of the Yearly Epistles, though not according to the practice of Quakers like the Gurneys. One can't help surmising that William Tuke's youthful ambition 'to live rather high' may have surfaced from the arduous repression which he had exerted, and bolted with him. It is fair to note that he and his family never lived there, to enjoy the space and trees and graciousness, though afterwards Superintendents generally did. Tuke was of course being generous with other people's money, though, as we saw, he was very ready to lend largely; but he was working with a Committee which met weekly, and which could presumably have restrained him, if they had thought fit; and the major decisions, like the move to accept necessitous patients *gratis*, were made by the quarterly meeting of subscribers. The wisdom from the point of view of therapy of providing generous physical comfort is surely indubitable; it is a philosophy that is evident at The Retreat today.

The Committee tried to attract extra support by two devices. One of them was an invitation to Friends to make contributions as annuities, carrying an obligation to pay 5% per annum to annuitants whom the donor names. This was an idea supported by Lindley Murray, who was intensely interested in The Retreat, and whose handwriting appears in many of the early drafts of business submitted to the Committee or to Tuke; he himself contributed £300 on these terms. The plan attracted gifts, but the payment of annuities were often a burden. The other scheme was to invite Friends' Meetings, especially Quarterly Meetings, to make 'a contribution of one hundred pounds . . . in a collective capacity', or to any Friend to donate twenty five pounds, or endow an annuity of fifty pounds, which would entitle them 'to nominate one poor patient at a time on the lowest terms of admission'. It is not clear whether this was ever taken advantage of.

As time went by they did get some legacies, which were a great relief, and 'several very liberal subscriptions were received at the latter end of the year 1797 and in the commencement of 1798'. The generous financing was aided a good deal by the organisation of the Society of Friends, with its constant comings and goings to Monthly, Quarterly and Yearly Meetings, also by the preaching journeys undertaken by leading Friends, all of which facilitated appeals for funds.

But things continued hazardous. Calculations had been based upon the assumption that in a normal year, when all the beds were filled, the running expenses of patients would be covered by their fees, and that the cost of admitting patients at half-fees, or gratis, would be covered by the larger fees, up to £1 a week, that would be paid for patients who wished and could afford a greater degree of comfort. But, partly owing to the war with France, it was some time before running costs were met from fees. This was first achieved in 1802, and then in most years from 1804, though in 1810 and 1812 the high price of food, caused by the war, prevented it. These adverse circumstances did not induce them to put up their fees. They continued in debt for twenty years, and more.

After 1813 they had an easier time. In that year Samuel Tuke published his *Description of The Retreat*, and more than that, it was reviewed in terms of unqualified and astonished approval by the Reverend Sydney Smith in *The Edinburgh Review*. This gave them splendid publicity; streams of visitors came to see the place; and application for admission was made by a large number of well-to-do patients, many of them not Quakers. It was decided to accept non-Quakers when there was space; and the enhanced fee which such patients paid helped the finances.

The attitude of the Committee to finance may be illustrated by two quotations. In the Annual Report for 1798, when they owed £1,300 on the buildings, and when patients' fees fell short of their expenses by £308.13.6., Tuke's comment was: 'The managers of the Institution could not but feel the most lively satisfaction, in thus witnessing in great measure the fulfilment of their hopes'. The Report says 'We feel encouragement from the liberal support which the Institution has this year met with'.

They learned to live with debt. In 1812 William Tuke, concluding his report as Treasurer, said: 'There is still a debt of £1,745.10.10 . . . I

51

confess, however, I do not wish to see The Retreat wholly independent of annual contributions'. He felt that they carried an assurance of interest and support which was a stimulus to those who worked there.

The main reason why The Retreat survived the precarious early years was that William Tuke had exactly the qualities needed by a man responsible for such a project. The Retreat was a challenge to him. The tea business never extended him or greatly interested him. His compassion, combined with his buoyancy and indefatigable energy and his gift for leadership, made him the ideal person for this demanding assignment. His grandson Samuel, who knew him very well, said 'No ordinary difficulties were likely to deter the founder of the institution'. When William Tuke undertook this work, he was elderly but he throve on it, and so did The Retreat.

CHAPTER V

Developments

IN the second year of The Retreat, two experiments were made which were very successful, and had a most beneficial effect upon the life and therapeutic practice there. These two developments were inter-dependent upon each other and consistent with Quaker principles. They were, first, the introduction of much milder methods of treatment, and second, the structure of a regime based upon human relationships rather than one in which fear was deliberately instilled into the minds of the patients.

These courageous decisions were not without precedent. In the early 1780s, the Hospital Bonifacio in Florence had given up the use of chains and fetters, and in 1793, Philippe Pinel, physician at the Bicêtre in Paris had also abandoned this form of physical restraint. William Tuke and his friends did not know of these events, at the time, because of the war which was going on. It is thought that some years later on, the Tukes did get to hear about Pinel, though it seems they never met him. On the other hand, it is believed Pinel learned about The Retreat as early as 1798, possibly through the visit made by the Swiss Dr. De la Rive in that year. Although therefore The Retreat was not first in the field with more humanitarian methods, its founder and staff were working on principles which they devised and developed themselves, and which they introduced by gradual, indeed tentative stages. Their courage in showing this initiative was beyond praise.

Dr. Fowler, having had little experience of treating the insane when he accepted his post as visiting physician, 'was determined', as Samuel Tuke said, 'to give full trial of the means which the superior knowledge of others had already recommended'. Therefore 'bleeding, blisters, seatons, evacuants and many other prescriptions, which have been highly recommended by writers on insanity, received ample trial'. Unlike most physicians of his time he kept careful notes on the condition of the patients before and after these treatments, from which he was unable to conclude that the remedies brought about any improvement. Moreover he was quite aware that the administration of them was a very difficult and disturbing business. Every time a patient had to be cajoled or compelled to submit to these disgusting ministra-tions, there would be protest and resistance, and the quiet of the ward would be likely to be destroyed by the noise and apprehensions that were excited. Another argument against them was, he felt, 'the impossibility of employing powerful medicine in a long continuance, without some injury to the constitution'. Dr. Fowler in the end gave orders that when patients objected very much to the treatments he had ordered, they were not to be compelled . Not very long after, he abandoned these physical treatments altogether. This was a great disappointment to him. He was reading widely on the subject of insanity, and had hoped for much from the cures he tried, one after another; and in the end he was obliged to admit that he could not treat insanity; he was led to 'the painful conclusion (painful alike to our pride and our humanity) that medicine as yet possesses very inadequate means to relieve the most grievous of human diseases'. One measure Dr. Fowler believed he had discovered that had a definitely beneficial effect was the warm bath for cases of melancholia. He encouraged the patient to stay in the bath as hot as he could bear it, for as long as he could bear it; and the record was an hour at 80 degrees. The work involved in providing all this hot water for such baths, and then disposing of it, is not easy for 20th century people to envisage, and it was certainly not common practice in those days to indulge in such goings on.

It was said that William Tuke was much impressed by this success. One might guess that the most creative thing Dr. Fowler did during his short time at The Retreat was his courageous abandonment of traditional treatment. Once these recurrent crises of treatment were abolished for good, Katherine Allen and her nursing staff could get on with their business of calm, good-tempered routine, and Fowler gave them consistent support. The people in charge at The Retreat believed that the delicate relationship between mind and body is particularly sensitive when the mind is disturbed, and that even a very slight indisposition could bring about a serious set-back to mental recovery; they sent for Dr. Fowler freely to cope with minor as well as major indispositions, so that his patients saw him often: he had great influence with them, and his goodness and gentleness must have been one of the potent factors in the therapeutic atmosphere which The Retreat enjoyed. Dr. Fowler died in 1802 as the result of a fall from his horse, and he was a great loss.

The second innovation was the abolition of fear as the basis of discipline and this was the work of George Jepson; it must have begun during the period when Dr. Fowler was moving towards his own change in medical policy.

Jepson had on his arrival found 'the regime of fear' taken for granted as the basis of management. He reacted against this principle. 'The investigating mind of George Jepson' (says *The Sketch*, 1828) 'had often previously to his appointment as Superintendent, led him to query the beneficial effects resulting from this method of management; he had observed that wild animals were most easily tamed by gentle methods; and judging by analogy, he inferred that man, bereft of reason, might be influenced by the same means. His own experience at that time was too slight to warrant him discarding a system sanctioned by general adoption. Yet on an occasion soon after his introduction to office, after the exercise of some severity towards a violent patient, he passed a sleepless night in anxious cogitations. He felt satisfied that his mode of treatment in this case had tended to irritate rather than control the patient's feelings; he determined to try the opposite system. In this conclusion he was strengthened by his observations made in visiting two of the large establishments in the metropolis and one in the vicinity of this city. Following steadily but cautiously the guidance of his judgment and feelings, his observation and experience soon led him to abandon the system of terror, and to adopt that which presumed the patient to be generally capable of influence through the kindly affections of the heart; and also in considerable degree through the medium of the understanding. Dr. Fowler entered heartily into the views of the committee and Superintendent in regard to the mild system of treatment . . . He was soon led to the conclusion that . . . more was to be expected in many cases through the influence of a judicious system of moral treatment, leading immediately to the alleviation of mental symptoms, than from the administration of medicine'.

One may note that it had 'often' occurred to Jepson before he came to The Retreat, that severity in the handling of the insane might not be the best way. This suggests that during the years at Knaresborough when he had ministered as an apothecary to patients who came to him from far and wide, to those who needed counsel as well as those who came for medical treatment, he must have had some who were mentally disturbed. Some of these he would have diagnosed not as ill but as unhappy, and these he would have comforted and counselled; others would have received such advice and medicines as he could offer; and some would have gone to private madhouses and come under the 'régime of fear'. He would probably have had some continuing knowledge of what became of them through their families, and thus come to doubt whether intimidation was the best basis of management. Thus his desire to try a gentler method of his own was probably not just idealistic kindness, but based on a certain amount of observation. He must have been able to see the effect of his own gentleness on such patients, before they became bad enough to be sent away. But he felt that his own experience was 'slight', and being a modest man was willing to be taught. His experience of remorse after exercising severity, brought his revulsion to a head, and he now took action. Modest man though he was he trusted his own judgment in the matter. He reported to the Committee the changes of method he proposed to introduce. The magnanimity of Dr. Fowler in supporting him must have influenced the Committee in giving him their agreement.

Thus within about two years, Dr. Fowler and George Jepson had abandoned both the orthodoxies which had governed the treatment of the insane. It was another great blow to The Retreat when Dr. Fowler died in 1802, after a relatively short period of service, but he worked there long enough to establish the new methods of treatment, which Jepson did all in his power to maintain.

Jepson, a true Yorkshireman, did not dramatise himself. He felt his way gradually. There are some beneficent changes that cannot be essayed unless there is an atmosphere of confidence in an institution: this atmosphere Jepson created. The daily management of patients was carried out with gentleness, from the time when they got up and dressed, or were helped to do so, right through the day. Some had meals at common tables, some in their rooms, to be supervised to prevent altercations developing into fighting; some of them would have to see the doctor, some to be set to work on various occupations. In all this he observed their reactions to kindness and soon changed his ideas about the condition of their minds; he saw that they were not like wild beasts, nor bereft of reason. They were human beings in whom reason had been impaired but not destroyed. He found that by appealing to their reasonableness and affection and their desire to be respected, he could give them confidence and gain their co-operation.

His contact with a new patient generally began on the doorstep. By the time the patient had got there he had probably had a long uncomfortable journey, perhaps of several days and nights, in chains or under other restraint, perhaps tightly confined in a strait jacket; in poor shape, fatigued, possibly bruised, angry, and as Samuel Tuke said 'vociferous'. Jepson told Samuel Tuke that the noisier a patient was the more he found it wise to soften his own voice. He had the restraints removed at once, and civilly invited the newcomer to a meal with the Family. He took him to his room and had a talk with him, making it plain that he did not want ever to have to put restraint upon him again, that he hoped he would be comfortable, and so conduct himself that there would be no need for restraint. It became plain to the patient that it did indeed rest with him whether or not he should continue to enjoy this new freedom. One of the miseries of mental illness is often the loss of standing as a normal human being, which leads to the loss of self-respect. Jepson's patient would realise that he was being treated with respect. Jepson was thus exploiting the moment of quiet, which can ensue upon arrival at hospital, in a way that was precisely opposite to that inculcated by orthodox methods, i.e. not to arouse but to allay fear. The effect was usually instantaneous. The patient complied. The shock of finding himself accepted as a sensible man would be followed by relaxation of tension, as the comfort of the place had its effect upon him: the good meals, the equable temper and civility of the attendants, the good bed, the pervading quiet. The great value of this is that for a personality in defeat, or nearly in defeat, it comes as a welcome surprise to be treated as significant; to be found interesting is a bit of an inspiration, it excites a wish to retain concern and approval; this is a moral tonic. A person in sore trouble, like someone who is mentally ill, can find new motivation for making an effort to do better, to win praise, to shake off apathy.

But the quiet of an asylum may not be all to the good. One of the depressing features of life in a mental home, as it strikes the visitor, is the silence in which some patients sit for hours. Not doing anything nor wishing for greeting or conversation. Patients sometimes find themselves shut up in an oppressive silence which they don't know how to break; they may often be longing for a chance to talk, especially about themselves. Jepson recognised this condition as depressive, and thought it important that patients should have something to think about to divert their minds away from their own thoughts, which were doing them no good. He developed occupational therapy. This had probably begun before he got there, in the women's day room. With so much sewing and knitting and mending to be done, at a time when there was no trade in cheap, machine-made clothes, Katherine Allen, or Ann Retton before her, would have enlisted the co-operation of some women patients to help with it. Part of Jepson's gift was his ability to perceive and understand the experience that other people were having, and he would have seen that it did them good to have work to do. It became a policy to provide occupation. But it was not so simple to devise tasks for the men. Much of the work men do requires tools, some sharp, some heavy, most in some degree dangerous. Jepson thought that the work that gave the men most benefit was gardening,but they could not be trusted with spades and hoes without careful supervision, and the gardener was unsympathetic, and unwilling to be bothered with them. However, Jepson did find outdoor work for some of the men, presumably putting them under the care of another of the male staff; and basket-making was set up as an indoor job for them. Jepson would sometimes take a man for a long walk, and this, though not as good as gardening, would do him good. The exercise of the big muscles induces a sense of well-being.

It is noticeable that the work Jepson got his patients to do was needed in the life of The Retreat, and when they complied they were sharing in the necessary activity of the community, just as the sane, who were working beside them did. Samuel Tuke had interesting comments to make on the value of work as a therapy, in *A Letter on Pauper Asylums* (1815), 'The employment of insane persons should as far as it is practicable be adapted to their previous habits, inclinations and capacities . . . The greatest benefit will, I believe, be found to result from the patient being engaged in that employment in which he can most easily excel . . . whether it be an active or a sedentary one'.

There was another way in which Jepson promoted the comfort and therapy of The Retreat. He gave constant loving attention to each individual patient. His treatment was based on a personal relationship of confidence, a matter which cannot be too frequently stressed. It is by no means true that the main key to humane treatment is in the absence of physical force. Patients can be subjected to maddening assaults on their dignity — deprivation of privilege without due cause, verbal harshness, sarcasm, snubs, insolence. Jepson made a point of listening to patients, leading the conversation, when he could, to a topic on which they could speak with knowledge, offering them, in his kind way, a sort of deference; he wanted to build up what he called their 'self-complacency'; he thought it needed building up. He did not invite familiarity, which would have damaged the authority in him which they relied on. Samuel Tuke said he combined, in a remarkable way, firmness with gentleness.

He did not find it was any use at all to appeal to their reason to dispel delusions. This applied both to the macabre or ridiculous hallucinations of some, the melancholy notions of others and the conviction of the enmity of all mankind, which is the distressing misery of the persecution complex. Some insane people use the most ingenious logic to build into their own fantastic picture of their world whatever is said or done; yes, So and So did a kind thing, but only to deceive; yes, some doctors have seemed to do good to their patients, but only because they wanted their money; yes, Christ loves sinners, but not the damned; yes, they give you plenty of food here, but it is all poisoned. Jepson concluded that arguing only fixes their delusions.

The quietness of life was diversified by pleasant recurrent incidents: Jepson reading the Bible in his homely Yorkshire voice, of a Sunday afternoon: the monthly visit of cheerful and companionable women from York Meeting: the seasonal activities in the garden and the farm.

What was happening was that a community was being formed, a family, just as the founder had wished. This meant that positive personal relationships between the staff and the patients, and also amongst the staff and amongst the patients, were becoming part of the life at The Retreat. This general concern, both for the individual and for the community, was gradually, perhaps imperceptibly, contributing to treatment and therapy.

In 1806 George married Katherine Allen, after a fairly persistent courtship: she refused him at least once, but encouraged by the ever-understanding Lindley Murray, George tried again, with success. Their partnership became a feature of life at The Retreat; they worked together in close co-operation, and Katherine seems to have given George increased confidence. She was robust and good-humoured and everybody thought her clever at her job. In 1811, a French visitor, Louis Simond, took Jepson for a 'keeper' and thought he was completely under the authority of Katherine. 'The mistress of the house is a good-looking, portly lady, lately married to the keeper', he wrote. It is likely that she may have ordered George about a bit, but he did not show any sign of minding and while he may have learned a good deal from her, Samuel Tuke ascribed to George, with uninhibited admiration, all sorts of skills in management and policy. After their marriage, George and Katherine were able to strengthen the tradition of 'homeishness' in the place, and to develop still further the family atmosphere which enabled people to feel that they belonged there, and that they were valued. Soundly founded human relationships go a long way towards creating emotional security and diminishing the fears which make for stress.

Katherine had been in the habit of giving tea-parties from time to time. These often attracted attention. Samuel Tuke recorded that they were much enjoyed and that Katherine possessed 'an uncommon share of benevolent activity'. Everybody who was well enough was invited, everybody wore their best clothes, 'they vie with each other in politeness and propriety, the best fare is provided, the visitors are treated with all the attention of strangers. It rarely happens that any unpleasant circumstance occurs; the patients control in a wonderful degree their different propensities; the scene is at once curious and affectingly gratifying'. These tea-parties were continued by the Jepsons for many years and afforded the patients pleasant interludes of almost normal family life, with George acting as host, and Katherine as hostess.

There were incidents, however, that could be critical, and that called for special skill, ingenuity and courage. One of these hazards was the danger of violence.

In our own mental hospitals this has abated in recent decades by the discovery of successful sedative drugs, which were unknown in Jepson's day. It was the widespread fear of the violence of lunatics that made Sydney Smith express his admiration for 'the courage of the Quakers . . . and their contempt of danger'. Samuel Tuke confirms that the staff at The Retreat were fearless: 'The attendants at The Retreat feel themselves in no danger of injury from the patients who are unconfined; many of whom previously to their admission had been accustomed to much severity. No instance has occurred of any serious injury being done by a patient to any of the attendants; and at no period has there been manifested a general spirit of dissatisfaction or a tendency to revolt'. It is possible that this statement may have been somewhat over-optimistic, as The Retreat was not wholly free of incidents.

Later other asylums, which bravely gave up mechanical restraint, were sometimes less fortunate. Daniel Hack Tuke, in his *Chapters in the History of the Insane*, records a Government report on Asylums (1844 A): 'In asylums entirely disusing restraint . . . since the autumn of 1842 a patient and superintendent have been killed . . . a matron has been injured . . . another superintendent so bitten as to cause serious apprehension that his arm must be amputated, and two keepers injured so as to endanger their lives'. Dr. Conolly noted the danger in allowing deluded patients to walk about unattended, lest they mistake other people for those they hate, or for the devil. There were dangerous crises at The Retreat: Samuel Tuke quotes an incident which illustrates this. 'One patient discovered a ladder which he climbed, and thus he found himself staring into a room. A new attendant quickly brought him down; the patient was furious and started fighting, and if the attendant had not been quickly rescued by "the family" it is probable that "he would have paid for his rash act with his life"'. Dr. Kathleen Jones, Professor of Social Administration at York University, and author of *Lunacy Law and Conscience* and of *Mental Health and Social Policy 1845-1959*, has noted other instances of assault, especially by a patient called Wilson Sutton. '1814, 12 Aug. Today after a walk in the country and eating a good dinner, while the attendants were at theirs, he became quarrelsome — struck Josh Whiting, hurt Saml . . . After this time he was shut up in a room to get calm'. '1815, 15th January: When S L has come in sight he has fallen upon him furiously with his fists. 20th February — seized Saml Smith his attendant and threatened to throw him downstairs, breaking his watch and chain and straining his thumb . . . 16th September Fetched him (Smith) a blow between the eyes, but when freed seized an iron fender and felled the unfortunate Smith with it'. These incidents, recorded in the Log Book, took place after the writing of the *Description*; and it seems that Wilson Sutton's irritability with Saml Smith was perhaps exceptional. But Dr. Jones concludes that attendants at The Retreat were expected to take such things as part of the day's work, and did. We must agree with Sydney Smith that these people were brave.

George Jepson told Tuke that he believed that the chief cause of violence in the mentally ill was provocation. There can be no sort of doubt that in many asylums provocation of patients by cruelty and insolence was incessant and unpardonable. But some illnesses, like mania, include phases of dangerous excitement and anger, which are not necessarily due to provocation. In others hallucinations or voices urge the ill person to murderous or suicidal acts. And in any case provocation is difficult to avoid. Patients may be pathologically touchy, or roused to fury by trivial causes — by something an attendant or another patient said, or by the refusal of privileges to which a patient has become accustomed, but which must be withdrawn because his condition has deteriorated. A very slight incident sometimes 'exasperates the violence of the patient and provokes . . . that feverish and sometimes furious irritability in which the maniacal character is completely developed; and under which all power of self-control is utterly lost'.

In coping with violence Jepson was fearless and full of resource, for example it was he who dealt with the patient who had flared up dangerously after being pulled down from the ladder. A few days later Jepson took him for a walk in the fields as he thought it would do him good to get out. The man again became annoyed and rushed off and picked up a large stone, threatening to hurl it at Jepson. 'The superintendent, in no way ruffled, fixed his eye upon the patient and advancing upon him commanded him in a resolute voice to lay down the stone.' As Jepson got nearer he slowly complied and then let Jepson take him back to his room.

Jepson could use authority, 'the power of the EYE'. He could also, like a Quaker, use silence and the peaceableness of his own nature. There was 'a man of almost Herculean size and figure . . . who was frequently very vociferous and threatened his attendants, who in their defence were very desirous of restraining him by the jacket. The superintendent on these occasions went to his apartment; and though the first sight of him seemed rather to increase the patient's irritation, yet after sitting some time quietly beside him, the violent excitement subsided and he would listen to the persuasions and arguments of his friendly visitor. After such conversation the patient was generally better for some days or a week; in about four months he was discharged and perfectly recovered.' If it took four months for the illness to pass and Jepson's sessions with him kept him quiet for only a few days or a week, it would seem that Jepson must have spent many hours with him patiently in this way. It would also seem that Jepson was good at persuasion.

The most freely used way of preventing a very violent patient from hurting himself or others was to get him into a bare, rather darkened room with a mattress on the floor and leave him there locked up for a time. The incessant watchfulness of the attendants enabled them to perceive the onset of a violent phase before it had fully developed, and this would make seclusion easier to manage by persuasion. Apparently attacks of this kind usually passed off in a few hours; that such a patient found his seclusion welcome was sometimes shown by his anger if someone came in to see how he was getting on, before he wanted renewed contact with others.

The Retreat had other resources as well. Jepson devised a set of straps which were not so hot and confining for the wearer as a straitjacket, and permitted him to move about, nor so heavy and ignominious as chains. Two of these sets, which survive today at The Retreat, look pretty daunting. There are very stout straps to go behind the shoulders and prevent the wearer from delivering a heavy blow; they have long closed sleeves, which would make it impossible to use the fingers to throttle anybody, or for any other purpose. The women, on the other hand, had green leather belts with straps to the wrists, long enough to give them some freedom to eat or blow the nose, but not long enough to fight very well.

Only Jepson ever confined a patient in this way; the attendants were not allowed to do it, and it was always his wish to get the leathers on with the patient's consent and without a struggle. If there was likely to be resistance, Jepson would get so many attendants to help that the patient would see that he hadn't a chance and accept it. Samuel Tuke says the women thought their green belt and wrist straps rather smart, and it seems a triumph of humanity to invent a restrictive device which the patient will be pleased to accept as an enhancement of her dignity. All this is in strong contrast to what John Conolly had witnessed (not at Hanwell) when patients had to be restrained: 'After a violent struggle the patient was overcome by main force; his limbs secured by attendants with a tightness proportioned to the difficulty they had encountered; and the patient was left heated, irritated, mortified and probably bruised and hurt without one consoling word; left to scream and shout and execrate and apparently to exhaust his whole soul . . . '.

But Jepson could exercise force upon a patient, to get the leathers on him or take him to a secluded room with the help of several attendants, without losing the confidence of the patient or others. Samuel Tuke says there was as a rule little resentment when restraints were used. This assertion, as much as anything in the *Description*, disclosed the degree of confidence which Jepson had achieved. A patient was always helped to see that there was no wish to confine him, and if at the sight of the leathers a patient becoming violent promised to quieten down, Jepson always respected his promise and put them away. He was generally justified in his confidence, but he told Tuke he would rather take a risk than put a patient under physical restraint unnecessarily. Samuel says: 'I have known a patient, such is their sense of honour and moral obligation, hold for a long time a successful struggle with the violent propensities of their disorder'. It was believed that such difficult self-control was a factor that helped towards a cure.

Daniel Hack Tuke says that one of the ways of controlling patients was 'the guarded use of drugs'. Drugs presumably means opium in some form. The only mention of it in the *Description* is in a passage where Samuel says that 'the unpleasant effects frequently produced by the use of opium are well-known to the physicians': the implication seem to be that it was not used at that time at The Retreat, but this is not clear.

The importance of food, as we saw, was fully recognised and the meals were ample and varied. Food was very cleverly exploited to help to overcome one of the difficulties of manic disturbance. The manic patient cannot sleep, but sleep is what would help him most. 'It occurred to the sensible mind of the Superintendent, that all animals in a natural state repose after a full meal, and reasoning by analogy he imagined that a liberal supper might prove the best anodyne. He therefore caused a patient, whose violent excitement of mind indisposed him to sleep, to be supplied freely with meat or cheese and bread and good porter.' This was successful and was afterwards often used. Thus behaviour which would ordinarily invite punishment, under Jepson led to a treat.

With some patients food was a major problem in another way. These were the sufferers from anorexia nervosa, an illness which gives the patient such an aversion to food as can lead to death. At The Retreat kind persuasion would usually induce these patients to take food, or they could be stimulated to do so by being told not to, or by being allowed to steal it from the larder. But sometimes forcible feeding became necessary to save a life. 'This is perhaps the most painful duty which the attendant has to perform.' An apothecary called John Rogers, who gave evidence to the Select Committee (1815/6) said he had worked at four asylums in London and described forcible feeding as he had seen it done. 'They have a vessel resembling a teapot, sometimes with a long spout, I have seen it with a short one; the patient is laid on his back and held down by two keepers. One has a cloth in his hand, one a large key for opening the mouth; the spout of the pot is forced into the mouth, the nose is held by the assistant keeper, and the cloth immediately slapped over the mouth; in this state the patient must either swallow or die, unless they desist. I have seen them black in the face . . . till they have been at the point of death; my opinion is that sometimes they force the spout of this thing too far and the food passes down the windpipe and suffocation ensues . . . Mrs. Hodge died while Mary Seal was forcing her. I do not know of any other method except coaxing. They sometimes force them four or five times a day.' Haslam said he had seen a number of women, 'who having suffered a temporary derangement and undergone the brutal operation of spouting, in private receptacles of the insane, have been restored to their friends without a front tooth in either jaw. Unfortunately the task of forcing patients to take food or medicine is consigned to the rude hand of an ignorant unfeeling servant. It should always be performed by the master or mistress of the madhouse'. Jepson did it himself. He had the patient on a rocking chair and used a key to open the mouth. His assistant passed food in a liquid state in a strong spoon into the patient's mouth; it was necessary to get the point of the spoon halfway over the tongue, or the patient would spit it out. Tuke says there was seldom occasion for the frequent repetition of the operation.

Patients were always encouraged to eat as much as they wanted. Permissiveness in a matter like this does a great deal to instil confidence in the management.

Among the means used at The Retreat to help patients, Samuel Tuke noted 'the mild but powerful influence of the precepts of our holy religion. Where these have been strongly imbued in early life', he says, 'they become little less than principles of our nature; and their restraining power is frequently felt even under the delirious excitement of insanity. To encourage the influence of religious principles over the mind of the insane is considered of great consequence as a means of cure . . . Many patients attend the religious meetings of the Society held in the city', (this is still the case) 'and most of them are assembled on a First Day afternoon, when the Superintendent reads to them several chapters of the Bible. A profound silence generally ensues'. Jepson must, I think, have had a beautiful voice or he could not have held them for the length of several chapters. However, listening to the Bible read aloud was a common Quaker practice. Elizabeth Fry read so beautifully that she was always asked to do so, not only at Newgate, where her prisoners knew her well and loved her, but wherever she went on religious journeys. We note that the patients at The Retreat were quiet not only during the reading, but afterwards; this silence which 'ensued' was of course common Quaker custom; these patients, many of them very poor, had been taught to regard corporate silence as a normal form of prayer, and had learned to practice it from childhood up.

It is noted in the Case Book that some patients had a habit of speaking in Meeting. This can be a bit disturbing, because the communications of the insane are sometimes odd. York Friends are always glad to share their Meeting with people from The Retreat.

DESCRIPTION

OF

THE RETREAT,

AN INSTITUTION NEAR YORK

For Insane Persons

OF THE

SOCIETY OF FRIENDS.

CONTAINING AN ACCOUNT OF ITS

ORIGIN AND PROGRESS,

The Modes of Treatment,

AND

A STATEMENT OF CASES,

By SAMUEL TUKE.

With an Elevation and Plans of the Building.

YORK:

PRINTED FOR W. ALEXANDER, AND SOLD BY HIM;
SOLD ALSO BY M. M. AND E. WEBB, BRISTOL:
AND BY DARTON, HARVEY, AND CO.; WILLIAM PHILLIPS; AND
W. DARTON, LONDON.

1813.

CHAPTER VI

The Impact of The Retreat

IN 1811, Henry Tuke suggested to his son Samuel that he should write a history of The Retreat, which had then been running for fifteen years.

Henry himself was a writer, who had in the last decade published a number of books about Quakerism. His *Principles of Christianity* was much loved. There is a copy of it at The Retreat, a small leather-bound volume tooled in gold, inscribed by Henry to George Jepson. One wonders how it got left behind when the Jepsons retired to Leeds ten years later. It appears that Samuel did not at first wish to write about The Retreat, although he had been deeply interested in mental illness for some years. He was greatly pre-occupied as a man of business, while his father was giving so much time to the Society of Friends and to The Retreat itself, and he was also undertaking religious journeys to visit other Meetings, and keeping in touch with Quakers far and wide. However, most fortunately Samuel did not feel that he could refuse his father's request.

Samuel was twenty-seven and had been a partner in the family business since 1805. He took the matter of this new book very seriously, and immediately gave up the study of Hebrew, which he had been learning, in order, as he says in his *Memoir*, to be able to read 'at least the poetical parts of the Old Testament in the original'. He was a great reader, and he now set himself to the study of insanity, by consulting books and by visiting asylums, as a main commitment of his life. Almost the first thing he did in this new undertaking was to invite George Jepson to dinner. 'We had much conversation on the subject of insanity'. These studies were effective. When the book, *Description of The Retreat at York*, appeared, it was widely assumed to be by a medical man, which must have been gratifying to Samuel who had wished to be a doctor. It was 'Printed for W. Alexander in York', in 1813, the year before Henry's death. William Alexander was Samuel's uncle by marriage, the husband of Ann Tuke, who had made the original suggestion that The Retreat should be founded. The book was republished in 1964, by photo-lithography by Dawsons of Pall Mall.

The *Description* opens with an account of the foundation of The Retreat, followed by a chapter on the house and grounds. These were, we saw, an expression of originality in the thinking of William Tuke, combining freedom for patients with security. Samuel believed that the design of asylums had a profound effect on the management of patients and the kind of life they led. He wrote *Notes on the Design of Asylums* for the Wakefield County Council in 1812, and they consciously followed the example of The Retreat in the building and organisation of their own asylum. Samuel did not think the design of The Retreat was faultless: he regretted that the galleries had small rooms on both sides, which provided a number of patients with rooms of their own, but which made the galleries necessarily dark. He commended the planning of the asylum in Glasgow, which had windows all along one side of its galleries. He also thought the courts at The Retreat appeared too small and admitted too little variety. He remarks that the design of many asylums have faults arising from 'excessive attention to safety'. 'People in general have the most erroneous notions of the constantly outrageous behaviour or malicious disposition of deranged persons.'

There follows a short chapter on Dr. Fowler's experiments with the then orthodox treatments, and his conclusion that they did no good. It was probably wise to give this theme ample discussion, because otherwise there might have been criticism of The Retreat for neglecting them. There was, however, already an increasing doubt about these age-old remedies, as we have already seen. Samuel nowhere claims that The Retreat was the *first* institution to venture on mild management of the insane, and in this he was quite right, for Dr. Ferriar and Dr. Fox had already made some progress in using more humane methods. Samuel naturally enough did not describe these, because he was not compiling a history or general survey of mental hospitals and treatment, but giving a picture of The Retreat.

The heart of the book is the long section on the work of Jepson. Samuel says: 'Many benevolent men in many places have too long been dissatisfied with the system of management generally pursued, but benevolent theory was powerless when opposed by practical experience', though, he adds, 'the man of long experience may be narrow and mistaken'. Jepson, he says, 'had by his talents and humanity carried into effect the benevolent wishes of the original founders of this Establishment beyond their most sanguine expectations . . . Had I not been assured of his cordial assistance the work would not have been attempted . . . It affords me some satisfaction to reflect that some at least of his knowledge is now communicated'. The acknowledgements to Jepson continue throughout the book: 'The Superintendent says . . .'.

The author politely explains that George himself was too busy to undertake to write up his own work, and this was certainly true. But it is doubtful whether George could have written a book, even if he had nothing else to do. Such scraps of his autograph as survive are in a small wavering script, the hand of a man who does not very confidently or with pleasure put pen to paper, quite unlike Samuel's racing business copperplate. One should record, however, that George undertook a good deal of correspondence with the relatives of patients.

Samuel was in no doubt as to the success of his grandfather and the staff. He unequivocally stated his case: 'The Retreat has demonstrated beyond all contradiction the superior efficacy, both in respect of cure and security, of a mild system of treatment, in all cases of mental disorder'. This is a strong statement. How could he know this?

Today such a claim would have to be supported by carefully kept and closely reasoned statistics, and The Retreat figures would have to be compared with those of other hospitals. Statistics are numbers, and you cannot have them unless you are dealing with things or events that can be counted. For instance, admissions, discharges, deaths and abscondings can be counted. But they do not tell you what you want to know. If you do not think it worth while attending to changes that cannot be expressed in statistics, you will miss a great deal, perhaps the most important aspects of a problem.

Samuel Tuke gives some careful statistics for The Retreat. He says that from 1796 to 1811, 149 patients had been admitted, sixty of whom had only recently become ill, and eighty-nine who had been ill for some time. Of the sixty recent cases, forty recovered and eight improved. But it was impossible to compare these figures with those of other hospitals, partly because it was not a common practice to keep such records, and partly because, where records were kept, they were based upon different classifications of mental condition. St. Luke's, for example, records the proportion of 'cures' to admissions of patients who arrived 'in a curable condition'. This is such an imprecise qualification that the record is useless for comparison with those of other places. Bethlem kept records of admissions and discharges but not of treatments; but Bethlem patients were commonly discharged after a year, whether they were better or not. However, it so happened that the Bethlem apothecary, Mr. Gozna, had for his own interest kept a private record that was much fuller, for patients from 1772 to 1787. From his study of these figures, Dr. Black deduced that 'two-thirds of all patients in the first attack will recover within twelve months . . . if left to the unassisted efforts of nature'. Macalpine and Hunter (who discuss these figures: *George III and the Mad Business*, p. 297 ff) confirm that Black's conclusion is borne out by general experience. 'Of one hundred psychiatric patients taken at random, one-third will recover completely, one-third will recover, but not to their previous level, and one-third will remain impaired or get worse.' The patients at The Retreat were of course untreated from the medical point of view after Dr. Fowler gave up his attempts to apply the usual remedies. Dr. Black's book, *A Comparative View of the Mortality of the Human Species of all Ages; and of the Diseases and Casualties by which they are Destroyed or Annoyed*, was published in 1788. At this time the Tukes were not yet concerned with insanity, the book appears not to have been in their library, and when Samuel was reading all he could lay hands on about mental illness, he did not find Dr. Black's book; so he did not realise that anybody had considered whether there was an average rate of recovery or improvement for these illnesses. In fact, the figures he quotes for The Retreat seem to show a better than average rate of recovery and improvement, according to Dr. Black's standard.

But Samuel must have formed his very definite opinion not from figures but from other kinds of evidence, mainly observation. For one thing, by 1811, the staff at The Retreat had tried both the severe old system and the new mild method, which Jepson had developed, and they had no doubt at all which produced the better results. For another, William Tuke and George Jepson got a good deal of information from patients who came from other hospitals, and from their relatives; they both visited other hospitals. Moreover, The Retreat was visited by a stream of people, many of them well-informed or with medical knowledge and an interest in asylums and madhouses.

But the Quakers' concern was not merely with recoveries; they realised that for many patients, especially those who had been ill a long time, there was no prospect of recovery. What they wanted to achieve was that their patients should have their illness in comfort. The First *Annual Report* (p. 56) says, 'The generality of patients whose illness is of long standing have little or no prospect of a perfect recovery; yet divers of these appear more comfortable to themselves and are improved in their mental faculties'. It was noted that those far gone in witlessness could be easily amused and become fond of their attendants. 'Even in those deplorable instances where the ingenious humanity of the superintendent fails to conciliate, and the jaundice-like disease changes the very aspect of nature, and represents all mankind as the leagued enemies of the patients, the existence of the social affections had often been strikingly evidenced to some of the inferior animals.' On the other hand, and The Retreat staff must have known this, there are sometimes cases where it is necessary to keep such patients away from animals, because there is a danger that they may torment them. This is a danger which constant surveillance can check.

There are mental illnesses which produce such severe alienation that nothing anybody can do or say can comfort the patient. Modern drugs can assuage this condition with sedation, but, as we have seen, the only drug then known to be effective was opium, and the addictive effect of this was so well understood that the doctors were unwilling to use it.

The patient's point of view is illustrated in a letter from E. Chaper (dated 20.1.1799). Though this records the experience of only one man, it is worth noting: he had tried to work up local interest in The Retreat, with a view to raising some financial support, but had failed. 'I have expressed to divers that the sense of quietude and comfortableness in the House is far beyond anything which I would have thought possible. But the Friends have not been able to feel for themselves what a desirable (yea, I think an unspeakably desirable) situation The Retreat is, for any person under the affliction of mental maladies . . . I often gratefully remember all your kindness to me when at York, and would be glad to return some of it at Amersham.' (Retreat Papers)

Samuel Tuke does not give figures for abscondings, though from 1808 it was an offence against the law to allow a lunatic to escape; the public fear of lunatics seems to have been lively. Visitors to The Retreat noticed that patients were not chained or leg-locked, that the estate had no high wall, the front door was not locked. It looked like a country house. But there were precautions, which, for the sake of the patients' feelings, were deliberately kept inconspicuous. The window-bars were invisibly reinforced, there were inner courts that were enclosed, for patients known to be at risk; above all there was an adequate staff for constant surveillance. However, it is interesting that Thomas Bakewell, in evidence to the House of Commons Select Committee, said that there were some kinds of mental illness which involved restlessness and a propensity to wander. He said that 'when paroxysms are coming on patients feel uneasy and think they should be better anywhere else'. The Retreat seems to have regarded this restlessness as part and parcel of mental illness. Absconders would never get very far, and apparently George or Katherine, as the case might be, had little difficulty in finding them and bringing them back. The poet Charles Lloyd was a patient at The Retreat for two periods and it would seem that he in his madness was given to wandering. There is a little pencilled note from him to Mrs. Jepson, written on one of these occasions, when he had found his way to the house of a friend, 'Do come and fetch me, I am miserable here, do come; do come; do come'. The *Description* (p. 154) says of another patient; 'The poor man rambled several times from the grounds of the Institution; which in his state of mind excited a considerable anxiety in the family (family means not his own family, but the community at The

Retreat). Of course it became necessary to confine him more within doors. He frequently walked out however'.

In his final chapter Samuel discusses the causes and classification of mental illness. He was quite baffled in the attempt to distinguish causes, but became convinced that the records at The Retreat did not support the currently common view that Methodism, then an exciting form of religion, and/or drunkenness were the most frequent causes of insanity. The Retreat doctors distinguished three types of mental illness, dementia, melancholia and mania, but this distinction and the symptoms associated with them are, I understand, of no medical value.

If it had been left to the Quakers to advertise to the general public the aims and achievements of The Retreat, they might not have got very far. But it was not left to them. A number of factors combined to bring them into public notice. The first of these was Samuel Tuke's book. This was not written to advertise The Retreat, but to satisfy the demands of people who kept writing to enquire about its work, probably mainly people who hoped to find in it a place where they could take afflicted relatives. But no writer could have wished for a more gratifying review than the *Description* got within a few months of its publication. This surprisingly came from the Reverend Sydney Smith, a strange and formidable character; clever, sometimes malicious and probably the most amusing clergyman who ever lived. He became known as the Smith of Smiths. He moved in the highest circles and was a valued habitué of Holland House. But his irrepressible wit apparently got in the way of his preferment, until through Lady Holland he obtained the living of Foston, near York. There he became, he says, 'village clergyman, village doctor, village comforter', for twenty years, built the charming rectory, and brought up a happy family of boys and girls. He was not highly paid and building the rectory used up his reserves; he added to his resources by taking schoolboys into his home to prepare them for the university, and also by writing frequently for *The Edinburgh Review*, which he had helped to found. This was the most famous of the literary reviews, at a time when highbrow journalism was becoming fashionable.

When the *Description* came into his hands, Sydney Smith saw at once, prince of journalists that he was, that whereas lunatics were news, and Quakers were news, Quaker lunatics were a rare scoop. He determined to write an article for the *Review* on The Retreat, and entitled it *Mad Quakers*. But first he rode out to see the place, or perhaps drove; he fell off his horse so often that in the end his family persuaded him to give up riding. He was deeply impressed. 'The Quakers', he said, 'are always ready with their money, and what is of far more importance, with their time and attention . . . for every variety of human misfortune. In this instance they have set an example of courage, patience and kindness which cannot be too highly commended or too widely diffused.' For William Tuke and for George and Katherine Jepson, Sydney Smith had the warmest admiration. He raised the question why it was that Quakers always did whatever they undertook to do better than anyone else. He concluded that this was partly because they took more pains, and partly because they were a rich society. He was not entirely justified in his idea that the Quakers were rich — there were, of course, some who were well off because of their business acumen, but the Society of Friends included many people of limited means. Sydney Smith was confident that 'the example of The Retreat will bring into repute a milder and better method of dealing with the insane'. This was a self-fulfilling prophecy. His article attracted to The Retreat a stream of visitors, from this country and abroad, some of them of high rank. In 1814 a royal party of Russians, including a princess and the Physician and Chamberlain to the Emperor of all the Russias, arrived to see The Retreat. In 1815 Robert Owen, the cotton manufacturer who founded the New Lanark model village, came. In 1816 the Grand Duke Nicholas arrived with a large suite; and two years later the Grand Duke Michael. Elizabeth Gurney (Fry) came several times with her father. And many others. All this was very valuable publicity for The Retreat. It attracted an increasing number of well-to-do patients, who were willing to pay higher rates and received more amenities, and sometimes brought their own attendants. Their fees significantly eased the financial difficulties, which were, of course, largely created by generosity to very poor patients.

As to the general level of well-being, the evidence of visitors was overwhelming. They were astonished at the placidity and contentment that pervaded the place; quite unlike anything they had seen before or could have imagined. Dr. Duncan of Edinburgh, for instance, said that 'The Retreat has demonstrated beyond contradiction the very great advantage resulting from a mode of treatment . . . much more mild than was before introduced to almost any asylum either at home or abroad'. William Stark, an architect, who visited many asylums while he was designing the asylum called Gartnavel at Glasgow, said of The Retreat, 'A great deal of delicacy appears in the attention paid to the smaller feelings of patients . . . Attachment to the place and to the managers, and an air of comfort and content (are seen there) . . . a government of humanity and consummate skill'.

Interest in The Retreat was further stimulated, in an indirect and most unlikely way, by Dr. Best, the physician of the York Asylum. He read the *Description* and in it he found a cap which fitted, and unwisely he put it on. He wrote to the York Herald (23rd September, 1813) to say that the *Description* implied unmerited aspersions on the York Asylum. Samuel Tuke replied to the paper saying that there had been no such intention, nor really any implication; but Dr. Best could not let the matter rest, and wrote again. He was unlucky. A magistrate of the West Riding, Godfrey Higgins had, some months earlier, committed a man to the asylum. This man had assaulted an old woman, and Higgins concluded he was not of sound mind. But he was in good health. When Higgins saw him later, he was shocked at his physical deterioration; he wrote a letter of protest to the Governors. The Governors held a meeting at which this letter was read out, and they summoned some of the servants, who swore on oath that the man had been treated 'with all possible care, attention and humanity'. The Governors, including the Archbishop of York, who was in the chair, were satisfied and supposed that that settled the matter. But it did not. It only excited the public to conclude that the authorities of the asylum could not be trusted.

At this juncture somebody discovered that anyone could become a governor of the asylum by paying a subscription of £20. Thirteen citizens of York, including Godfrey Higgins and William and Samuel Tuke, paid their £20, not a small sum, and turned up at the March 1814 Quarterly Meeting of the Governors, demanding to be admitted. There was some argument as to whether this was perhaps irregular. But they got in. The meeting which ensued was difficult, but the Archbishop presided with courtesy and calm, and agreed with the new members that a committee of enquiry should be set up to look into fresh cases of alleged cruelty, which Higgins had collected. It was further agreed, by a margin of one vote, that there should be a general investigation into the system on which the asylum was run.

The result of this enquiry was a horror story. Amongst other improprieties there were two sets of accounts which did not tally: Higgins proved that large sums had been misappropriated by Dr. Best. There were two sets of figures of deaths, one reported 221, but it was established that 365 had been buried. Godfrey Higgins and Samuel Tuke insisted on visiting the hospital and penetrating into rooms and cells that were locked up: they found exceedingly filthy and cruel conditions, and, at one point, Higgins had to retire to vomit. The day after the committee closed their examinations, December 28th, there was a fire. Dr. Best was thirty miles away, attending to a private patient, the steward was in his residence, four miles away, the apothecary was out for the evening, with his wife, and she had the keys. Many patients were locked in their rooms. Two of the four keepers were present, one old and asthmatic; the other, Dawson, risked his life and got many patients out. How the fire started was never established, it appeared to have begun in a lumber room full of flock, where no fire had been lighted for a fortnight.

The Quarterly Court considering this report was divided. Lord Wilton said, 'Why not pounce upon the head?' But there was an unexplained tenderness for Best; a motion was carried 'that no criminality attaches to Dr. Best for misapplication of funds'; he had merely made mistakes. He retired to found an asylum of his own. All the staff were sacked. Some governors felt that this was unfair; the staff were not to blame for Best's mismanagement and Dawson had risked his life. But the feeling prevailed that the staff had been so inured to harshness with patients that it was not to be expected that they could change their ways. The alternative was a wholly new staff; the governors recognised that it would not be possible quickly to find so many trained or experienced keepers, but it was thought that this was a temporary difficulty; the new staff would soon teach themselves. *The Sketch* says when the new staff were appointed, the Jepsons went over to the asylum 'to reorganise the work'. Samuel's *Memoirs* disclose that they were only there for part of a day. To give them an idea of what was expected William Tuke was asked to draw up a set of rules for them, which he did.

Astonishingly enough it was felt not to be a serious matter to ask a whole set of inexperienced men and women to teach themselves to manage the insane by doing it. This plan had worked at The Retreat. It was not difficult to recruit an adequate number of people. In no long time the governors were very pleased with the way the asylum was going on. The number of deaths had gone down, and this they attributed to the better general hygiene being practised by the new staff. Some of the patients were taken to places of worship on Sundays. A general improvement was noted and it was suggested in the very complacent first report on the new regime that this was due to the good judgment of the Visitors, who now, as at The Retreat, made regular visits. It apparently did not occur to any governor to compliment the new staff on their success, and the staff most probably would not expect this.

Thus the reform of the York Asylum was triggered off by the publication of the *Description*. There was already a good deal of general concern about the insane, and the York story was immediately written up in a book by Jonathan Gray. This caught the attention of a wide public and so the House of Commons set up a Select Committee to enquire into Madhouses, and in 1816 a second committee, to which reference has been made. (See pages 3, 6, 8, also Index.) The reports of these committees, on public asylums in 1815 and on private madhouses in 1816, revealed that while conditions in these places varied, the overall picture was grim. The Commissioners appointed after the 1774 Act had duly visited and reported, and this had done little good. As already stated earlier in this book, the Act had given the Commissioners no power to withdraw licences from the owners of these places if they refused to make improvements which the Commissioners required. The story which reached the Select Committee, of dreadful dirt, revolting smells, chains and other physical restraints, punishments, starvation, cold and general apathy, is overwhelming.

Against this background, the figure of William Tuke came before the public eye as a striking contrast. He gave evidence to the second of these enquiries, a noble figure, old and white-haired, widely revered as the originator of the mild method of The Retreat. 'Every day he walked, unaccompanied and unafraid and benevolent, through the wards, and everywhere eyes brightened and he was greeted with glad faces and loving greetings.' He said in evidence that he knew every patient by name.

The revelations of the Select Committees should have led at once to fresh legislation, to amend the manifest defects of the existing laws. In fact during the next ten years the House of Commons brought in bill after bill for this purpose, but the House of Lords threw them out. The Hansard reports of these debates show that as a body the Lords were deplorably lacking in compassion and decent feeling. Lord Eldon, for instance, said: 'There could not be a more false humanity than an overhumanity with regard to persons afflicted with insanity'. (Quoted by Jones p. 111, from Hansard June 12th 1819.) In the division that followed this debate fourteen peers voted in favour of the bill for the reform of madhouses and thirty-five against.

At last, in 1828, the County Asylums Act became law. This remedied defects in existing regulations. The Commissioners in Lunacy were empowered to withdraw licences from proprietors of madhouses who refused to accede to their demands for improvements, and with the help of this sanction, they did over the years secure far higher standards. The Act made it obligatory on County Authorities to set up public asylums, a number of which were largely modelled on The Retreat, both with regard to building design and also principles of management. Some Authorities seconded their officers to serve at The Retreat for a time to learn its skills. Very significant was the fact that Lord Ashley, who later, in 1852, became Lord Shaftesbury, was appointed a Commissioner, a duty he undertook most reluctantly, poor man, as he felt it was an utterly unwelcome and inescapable burden. Shortly afterwards he was made Chairman of the Commissioners. Thereafter, to the end of his life, he devoted much of his time to the care of the insane. In 1852, he made a great speech reporting immense improvements in County Asylums. He went so far as to say that if it fell to his lot to lose his reason, he would rather be confined in a County Asylum than in a private house. There are no records which suggest that Shaftesbury ever visited The Retreat, but it is clear enough that the impact of The Retreat was as productive of good results in the County Asylums as it was in very many of the privately owned establishments. In 1818, Samuel Tuke published a monograph on *The Design and Management of Pauper Asylums*, and this was one of the means by which The Retreat's ideas became widely known.

In 1847 the Commissioners in Lunacy reported: 'In several of the county asylums and hospitals the adoption of a more gentle mode of management was . . . the result of public opinion and of the example set by the managers of The Retreat near York. The able writings of Dr. Conolly have contributed greatly . . . We look forward to the abolition of restraint'. (D. H. Tuke, p. 220 *History of the Insane*). Daniel Hack Tuke quotes from the Ninth Report of the Commissioners the details of a particular case that interested them. 'A lady was visited by them in a private asylum, where they found her in a room by herself in a sadly neglected condition and frequently placed under mechanical restraint. Her habits were dirty and her opportunities for taking exercise few . . . The Commissioners ordered her removal to another asylum (The York Retreat), and about twelve months afterwards saw her there, and made an entry to the effect that since her admission she had never been in restraint or seclusion; that her destructive and dirty habits had been corrected by constant attention, exercise out of doors and association with other patients. The Commissioners found her quiet, orderly, clean, well-dressed and so much improved in appearance that they had some difficulty at first in recognising her.'

Dr. Conolly was a remarkable man. As a student of medicine at Edinburgh he had decided to specialise in the treatment of insanity and he visited The Retreat after reading the *Description*; this was in 1826, four years after the death of William Tuke. He was deeply impressed and re-read it many times. He also visited a number of other asylums and was often shocked at what he saw in them. In 1838 he visited a small hospital for the insane at Lincoln, where they had, in that year, categorically decided to ban all use of force. Where they got this idea is not clear, not apparently from The Retreat. The following year Conolly became head of the large asylum at Hanwell . . . He says that reflecting on 'that excellent *Description of The Retreat* near York . . . (and also) on what I had seen at Lincoln, I determined that whatever difficulties

77

there might be to encounter, no such restraint should be permitted at Hanwell'.

This did not turn out to be quite so difficult as he had supposed it might. He found a tremendous variety of instruments of coercion, ready in every ward to be used at the discretion of the attendant. Conolly had all these leglocks, hobbles, muffs, handcuffs and the rest collected and kept in a locked cupboard. Any attendant who wished could make use of them, but only by applying for the key and entering in a book the name of the patient and the date, and also the reason for using the instrument. Conolly was amazed at the triviality of the reasons given for applying physical restraint: one man would keep taking his coat off; a woman kept on drinking cold water, another was incessantly running up and down the ward. The use of coercion dropped dramatically when he instituted the book of records and in a matter of months there was no coercion at all. Conolly devised a generous programme of diversion and occupation. But he had a very difficult governing body, who would not allow him to appoint his own staff, or give him proper support. In 1856 he felt obliged to resign, and from then on devoted himself to lecturing and writing on the care of the insane. His books are intensely interesting. It seems likely that he did the cause of the insane more good by the publicity he brought to it than he could have done if he had continued to concentrate his time and his gifts on a single asylum. He constantly expressed his indebtedness to The Retreat, although he thought they were mistaken not to abolish the use of physical restraint entirely. He was convinced that attendants who may not use force to induce patients to comply with instruction, will quickly use their ingenuity to find other ways of persuading them. The Tukes at The Retreat were quite sure, human nature being what it is, that you could not be confident of invariably having attendants who could control wards without occasional recourse to physical restraint.

By 1842 eight County Hospitals had adopted the principle of non-restraint: these were Chester, Dorset, Kent, Middlesex, Norfolk, Suffolk, Surrey and Leicester. But the system did not become universal. There would seem to have been several reasons for this. For one thing the hospitals that did adopt the principle were not always completely successful, as we have seen. The medical profession were slow to be convinced that non-violence was really the best method for dealing with insanity. Similarly the Commissioners in Lunacy for some time did not give their support, though they were converted to it in the end. In the latter part of the century it gradually prevailed.

There were other considerations that delayed its acceptance as a policy. A very powerful one was the obsession with money. It costs more to run an asylum without physical restraint, because if you cannot keep patients under control mechanically, you have to have enough attendants to keep watch on them all the time, and to be able to go to more than one patient at once to prevent them from attacking one another or otherwise disturbing the peace. The Committee that were responsible for asylums, national schools and other public institutions, were apt to be lavish over the external appearance of their buildings, but thought that otherwise their chief obligation to the rate-payers was to keep down costs: a glow of conscious virtue seems to pervade their reports, when they record economies. For instance, Dr. Conolly's educational classes for his patients at Hanwell went on very successfully for five or six years, giving the patients something to enjoy, to think and chat about. Then the governors stopped them without explanation. They cost £150 a year. The total expenditure of the institution was £25,000. It seems a mean economy.

One feels that in addition to preoccupation with money, there is another factor in the human mind that tends to inhibit compassion. There is a sort of resentment, which may not be quite conscious, against the abnormal, the inadequate, the miserable, so that consideration for such people, the expenditure of money or skill on their behalf, is grudged. Shaftesbury speaks of his sad awareness that the House of Commons had tired of his appeals to their compassion, and of his efforts to get legislation to mitigate the wretchedness of helpless people who could not help themselves; the poor, the boy chimney-sweeps, children in factories, the insane.

One fact remains clearly established, namely that the Tuke family could never be included in Shaftesbury's list of people who did not care about the sufferings of the underdog in society. Samuel's book was one most influential contribution made towards the relief of these sufferings.

G. Jepson

CHAPTER VII

Crisis and Succession

BY the second decade in the 19th century, The Retreat's reputation was well-established, but the Committee had ample reason to feel deeply concerned about its future. William Tuke's admirable son Henry, who had done so much for the family, for the tea business and also for The Retreat, died in 1814, so another irreplaceable mainstay in William's life was gone, and Henry's wife, Mary Maria, outlived him by only a year. By 1816, the three people who had done most to secure success for The Retreat, were all feeling their years. William himself was in his eighties, George and Katherine Jepson had turned seventy, and none of them was immune to the erosions of physical and mental energy which come upon the elderly.

George Jepson had always carried a great variety of duties in the management of The Retreat. His main responsibilities were to run the institution, train and control staff, care for patients, compound medicines and carry out minor surgery, and also to keep the accounts. He had, as we have seen, great freedom for initiative, and both he and his wife were on duty by night as well as by day. Many odd jobs came his way. He undertook much correspondence with families, about fees and the coming and going of patients. Sometimes when a family applied for admission for a patient, Jepson and Dr. Belcombe, The Retreat's physician since 1802, together decided whether he was really insane, and also checked that he had no other illnesses: patients were asked to bring with them notes from their own doctors to certify these points, but this was not always done satisfactorily. It was often a tedious business to organise their departure, when it was thought that they were sufficiently recovered, because families were not always willing to have them back. In 1817, for example, Jepson was instructed to assist in finding suitable lodgings for Jane King. After resigning her post as housekeeper at The Retreat in 1798, she had made several attempts to support herself, including setting up in a small tea business. But she eventually came back to The Retreat as a patient. After some time the Committee became convinced that she was not in fact insane, whether she had ever been so or not. She had no family to help her, and then it fell to Jepson and William Alexander to make arrangements for her.

Jepson also had the task of finding staff to be appointed by the

Committee as they were needed, and of supervising workmen on such jobs as white-washing and other work about the buildings. When patients died, he made arrangements for their burial. The Retreat had its own burial grounds until 1855. Owing to the slowness of posts it was often impossible to get relatives informed in time.

But from about 1816, the Minutes of the Committee show that Jepson was gradually being relieved of some of these jobs. Senior people, like William Alexander, were doing some of the correspondence. Later, workmen were being supervised by Samuel Tuke and others. In 1816, a man called John Anderson was appointed, at a fee of ten guineas a year, to help Jepson with the accounts, and especially the annual balancing. There was anxiety about this matter. There was often a considerable deficit at the end of the year; in 1818, for example a shortfall of £458. It seems several times to have been the case that the Treasurer, William Tuke, made generous loans to meet the deficit: for example, on one occasion he lent £700. George Jepson also lent upwards of £200, over a period of years. It was believed that these deficits arose because patients' fees did not balance the running costs, as they were meant to; and while, of course, the numbers and affluence of patients varied, it was believed that the main factor was the cost of food, and this was seriously affected by the war with France. It was decided that the weekly expenses should be entered under headings, to facilitate the comparison of one year with another, and for this purpose a book ruled in parallel columns was bought. But the plan did not work. The Treasurer was William Tuke, who in his latter years became blind, and the actual clerical work must have been done for him by George Jepson and John Anderson, and the detail that was now being required seems to have been too much for them.

There survive at The Retreat very many small scraps of paper, of different shapes and sizes and often without business headings, recording small weekly purchases, and receipted to Jepson. It would be the easiest thing in the world for an untrained accountant, busy with many other matters, to mislay some of these and get into difficulty. William Tuke had, of course, intended in 1797 to train Jepson in accounting, and no doubt he did, up to a point, but the institution had grown greatly in size since then, and it is clear from his own records that William made quite serious mistakes in accountancy in his own business. Jepson had apparently given satisfaction for some twenty years, but now the Committee seemed to be uneasy about him. In 1822 the Minutes record that the accounts were not in proper order, and another book was bought for them.

In October 1820, the Minutes report that 'a serious accident having deprived the Institution of the services of the Superintendent, the

Institution to be visited daily in rotation by a panel of ten Friends'. An arrangement was made with a druggist to make up medicine for them, as owing to his accident Jepson could not now do this. Bills were receipted to various Friends, including William's son John Tuke. We do not learn from the Minutes what the accident was, nor hear any more about it, till March 1821, when there is an entry: 'Geo. Jepson having recovered from his accident, and able to walk about the house, the extraordinary visitation shall cease'. Oddly, about two months later, without comment, a precisely similar entry appears.

The idea that The Retreat could be satisfactorily managed by ten laymen, each taking a day once in ten days, was clearly unrealistic. In truth, it must have been carried on during Jepson's absence by Katherine and the rest of the staff. The panel of Quakers would have been mainly engaged in meeting visitors and paying wages. Samuel's *Memoirs* throw no light on this episode. Even allowing for the reticence of Quakers and for the brevity of the Minutes, it does seem strange that there was no allusion to the nature of Jepson's illness, nor to his progress.

To add to all the complications, on December 6th, 1822, William Tuke at last died, at the age of ninety. He had become blind, and although he retained his positive and optimistic attitude to the very end, he must have been taking a diminishing part in decision-making and active work for a considerable time. But his death marked the end of a period dominated by his magnificent personality. In the replacement of Jepson, the Committee were deprived of The Retreat's main source of inspiration which had guided them since 1792. On March 17th, 1823, a Minute reads: 'Several applications having been made for the office of superintendent, it is concluded to call a General Meeting for the purpose of considering them during or after the ensuing Quarterly Meeting'. Samuel Tuke was to make the arrangements for this discussion. There is no earlier note of Jepson's intention to retire. On June 23rd, 1823, it was decided to grant Jepson a pension of £50 a year for his life-time. His wife was to retire with him, after serving The Retreat with devotion and success for longer than her husband had. A General Meeting dated June 26th, 1823, records the procedure adopted for replacing Jepson and his wife and adds, 'We cannot allow our valued friends to retire from the important posts which they have filled for upwards of 26 years without expressing thus publickly, our sense of their faithful and beneficial services to the Institution, from which it will continue to derive important advantages'. Later, the Minutes have an entry for July 11th, 'G. and K. Jepson left yesterday'. They went to Leeds.

It strikes one as sad that the Jepsons left York, where one would have thought they must have had many loving friends. However, George had a nephew in Leeds, who once made him a hat. The fact that we have little knowledge about this nephew need not imply that the relationship between them was slight. George died in 1836 and Katherine survived him for several years, so, like William Tuke, both lived to a ripe old age.

The Committee of The Retreat, having had ample warning that they must soon lose the two men and one woman who between them had created its life and its tradition, would have been wise to have groomed someone for the succession. This they had not done. Indeed it would have been difficult for them to groom anybody while William was around. They had, in fact, sacked one attendant, who had thought himself a potential Superintendent; John Binns. He had been trained at The Retreat and then had nine months work with them, and he applied for the post. But it was felt that he would not do. The Minutes record that Jepson was asked to give Binns notice to leave as soon as he could be replaced; but he left almost at once, apparently before anybody had been found to carry on his work. One concludes that he had been told that he would not be promoted and his reaction to this made the Committee feel they would be better off without him.

Samuel's *Memoirs* reveal acute anxiety about this appointment. The Governors were indeed in a difficult situation. They needed a man of great gifts with mental patients; a man who could control the staff and train them, and hold their respect; one who could deal well with public relations, on which recruitment of patients depended. Their policy had never been to appoint staff of professional status, except in the case of the physician. Of course they could not afford appropriate salaries for well qualified people, and in general the pay they offered was not at all liberal. Samuel did not, on the whole, think this a bad thing. 'I have observed', he wrote, 'that the most successful managers of the insane have been those who were the most humble and unselfish; and it is only persons of this class who will ever effectually supply their intellectual and religious wants'. For the post of Superintendent, however, the Governors were now looking for a medical man, preferably a Quaker, with professional and personal qualities of a very high order, who would make the right impression on the relatives of patients in search of an agreeable home for some member of the family who was mentally ill. But although they had wide contacts within the Society of Friends, they failed to find such a one who wanted the post.

Samuel has a passage in his *Practical Hints on the Construction and Economy of Pauper Lunatic Asylums* (1815, p. 26), which reveals how strongly he felt the need of a Superintendent who could and would exercise firm control of attendants. 'There is I apprehend more danger of patients suffering from being under an inferior servant, than from each other . . . A perpetual desire to lessen personal exertion exists on the part of the servants of these establishments; and those who have not almost *lived* in an asylum can but faintly conceive the temptation to neglect, oppression and cruelty, which present themselves to those who have the care of insane persons . . . The business of the attendant requires him to counteract some of the strongest impulses of our common nature . . . I have rarely met an attendant, however humane and well-informed, who did not in greater or lesser degree err in this respect. It is evident that the only security of good conduct on the part of the attendants is more frequent inspection.'

Having turned down the application of Binns for the Superintendent's post, the Committee were left with three candidates, only one of whom, according to Samuel's *Memoirs*, was remotely possible. This was Thomas Allis, a man who proved to be far more gifted than seemed likely at first, and whose opinion of himself was, to say the least, over-modest. Once again, The Retreat was fortunate in finding a man capable of carrying its great responsibilities, despite initial doubts which influenced both the Committee and also the applicant himself.

Allis had been at school with Samuel Tuke, at Ackworth. Samuel was now a Governor of Ackworth, which needed a headmaster; he wrote to Allis to ask him if he would consider the post. Allis had had a school of his own, but had given it up, and was running a business selling agricultural machinery, and also a farm. He did not want the headmastership. On the other hand he said he was interested in the idea of becoming Superintendent at The Retreat. By his own account he had no qualifications for this work. At first he did not press his claim. He wrote a sort of testimonial for himself; he said he was 'about 35 years of age, having no medical knowledge, a man whose only approximation to such knowledge is a superficial knowledge of chemistry as a science; professing as he hopes just common rate abilities; with general knowledge and powers of perception and attention and perseverance about on a par with the generality of persons occupying the middle rank in our society in which rank most of his friends are to be found'.

He was married and had four children. Samuel was rather horrified at the idea of his bringing a young family to live in an asylum, and so far the post had been residential, involving night duties. Allis could not see the difficulty. He wrote: 'I am aware of the tendency to imitation in children, but I presume thou dost not mean that this tendency would be likely to become contagious and produce insanity in children?' He thought he could 'check such imitation' as well as other faults. It is

85

interesting that here again, history to some extent repeated itself. One of these children, Elizabeth, later married William Pumphrey, who was her father's chief attendant, and in her old age she wrote exceedingly valuable memoirs about The Retreat, which give us vivid and interesting accounts of its management in the second half of the 19th century.

Allis now began to find that his business needed a fresh outlay, for which he did not wish to borrow, and he decided therefore that he quite definitely wanted the post at The Retreat. He wrote to say that his wife's sister lived with them and therefore a cottage near The Retreat would meet their needs, and he would like to know 'at least the minimum salary in mind'. The only reason he could think of for supposing he would be equal to the job was that several of his friends had assured him that he would be. 'It will not, I presume, be expected that I should have felt any natural predilection for the work; such a predilection I should conceive impossible; though I think it very possible for a person entering as he should on its duties to be interested in the welfare of the Institution and of the unhappy objects in his care, and to become really fond of the employment.'

It was a Quakerly trait to give a very cool appraisal of oneself, and a Quaker would appreciate this, but even so Allis does not seem to have commended himself with much confidence. Yet his was the only possible application. One feels that the Committee's only recourse would have been to bring pressure to bear on Samuel Tuke to undertake to act as Superintendent, as his grandfather had done before him, until he could train someone to take his place. Samuel's home was five minutes walk away in Lawrence Street. But this was apparently not possible nor thought of. There was no one else in sight. Allis was therefore appointed. A surgeon was engaged to do the minor medical work that Jepson had done, coming once a week for £10 a year, and keeping a book to record what he did.

When any institution, hospital, college, school or business has created a life and tradition of its own, under the leadership of a very gifted personality, or several such people, and that person or persons has to go, there is always a danger that the tradition may be lost. It is not, of course, the case that it is invariably the best thing for an institution to go on unchanged. Times are bound to come when a living community will modify some of its ways; such developments are often most comfortably effected when there is a change of leadership. A time of change is necessarily a time of risk, but risks have to be taken if a person or an institution is to stay alive. However, for The Retreat at *this* time, the thing most devoutly to be wished was that it should preserve its special way of life, with its delicate syndrome of values. It needed what anthropologists call a culture-carrier, an individual gifted in leadership, deeply involved with the skills and customs of the place. Could Thomas Allis, a man obviously ignorant about the insane and their needs, be expected to understand and accept the ideals of The Retreat? If he were to introduce unwise or over hasty changes the traditions he inherited could be killed in a month. His earlier experience as a schoolmaster might seem to be a potential disadvantage because although the fact that he was accustomed to exercise authority would be helpful to him, he might so easily have felt that what was good for unruly boys would be equally good for the insane; and in those days schoolboys were usually controlled by flogging. The Retreat might have come again under a regime of fear, of severity and punishment, the antithesis of the confidence on which its life had been built. At the best, Thomas Allis could hardly have been expected at first to appreciate all that was good in the customary ways of The Retreat, though being a Quaker, it was natural for him to know the value of quiet and tranquillity. Would he realise the importance of organisation and administration? At The Retreat, for instance, there were enough staff to keep the patients under constant surveillance and yet allow them to move about with a fair degree of freedom; if patients cannot do this they become aggressive; but many asylums would not go to the expense of an adequate staff. Again, at The Retreat much trouble was taken to provide suitable occupation for men as well as women, though Jepson realised, as we have seen, that men's work, especially out of doors, often involves the use of heavy tools that could be dangerous, calling for very careful supervision: it would have saved trouble to say that this was impracticable. Such customs can be kept going if those in charge see the point and are prepared to take trouble. But it is probable that in many institutions good traditions are eroded and lost, because a new head fails to appreciate the significance of the customs he finds. The only people who are aware of such changes are likely to be the patients, staff, schoolchildren, or others who are affected by them, but who don't get sufficiently brought into consultation. The Retreat, however, survived the change from one Superintendent to another without trauma.

It seems necessary to reconsider Allis.

He certainly gave a bad impression of himself in writing, especially by his foolish remark that there could be no harm to children living among the mentally ill provided they were not permitted to mimic them. But the Committee were not entirely dependent upon Allis' letters: Samuel had known him a long time, and thought him quite fit to be a headmaster — although The Retreat was not a similar job. Much later, another man who had known him as a schoolboy at his school, wrote of him: 'He was unpolished in appearance and manners, a vigorous hearty man . . . I remember his kindness to me when I broke my leg . . . His heart went out to the boys who had left the school and I think his influence in this direction of considerable value'. Thomas Kitching, for many years a member of the Committee, remembered Allis and his wife in retirement, with very warm and grateful recollections of their kindness. 'In appearance he was a fine large man, with white hair and whiskers very straight, with kindly light blue eyes. He was particularly fond of boys and used to have parties of them to tea occasionally from Bootham School . . . He visited Ackworth General Meeting and had a commendable habit of presenting such boys as he knew with a shilling apiece. I was one.'

There was no doubt about his benevolence. His manners at The Retreat appear not to have been boisterous nor noticeably pompous (though one must remember that the 19th century liked pomposity in men). One visitor described him as 'a very courteous Quaker'. Mary Allis, his wife, was a kind woman; there was a boy of 13, who was brought to The Retreat as a patient, and when he was taken to his room he cried so bitterly that she brought him instead to their own house, and he was one of their family for seven years.

But benevolence is not enough. Skill and resource are needed in handling insane patients. Allis' task was not only to accept the tradition of quiet and gentleness, but also to be able to sustain it under assault, perhaps violent assault. For the custom was that the attendants kept constant watch on the patients and their changing moods, so as to intervene before rising tempers became inflamed, before shouting matches developed into fisticuffs; but when it happened that what they could do was not enough, and they were afraid a patient was becoming dangerous, they had previously had recourse to Jepson. This was a juncture where Jepson's 'consummate skill' was invaluable; he could rise to these occasions. But when he was gone, to whom would they go for help? To Allis. It was his job to underpin their efforts when they were at the end of their tether and could do no more. Failure to manage patients who were getting out of control would quickly have entailed noise and commotion. Moreover it was necessary for him to hold the respect of the staff, and this he succeeded in doing. He did make more use of seclusion for violent patients than Jepson had done, a policy which met with approval.

The Committee built more rooms for seclusion of excited patients, not entirely because of greater numbers. Jepson had latterly been responsible for sixty patients and generally there were not more than two to four in seclusion. Allis soon had eighty patients and provision was made for eight to ten to be secluded at one time. But the general atmosphere in the house was in fact unchanged, and some visitors were able to note that none of the isolation rooms was in use.

Thomas Allis must have been extraordinarily willing to learn. It is not easy as a rule for men and women in middle life, already accustomed to carry responsibility, to develop a new approach to a job. The person he must mainly have learnt from was Samuel Tuke. In fact Samuel was obviously the culture-carrier in chief. He had been deeply interested in insanity, for fifteen years; he had written the *Description*, and served on the Committee. At least as important as all these ways of studying the problems, he had, at one time around 1815, 'almost lived' at The Retreat. It is clear that he had himself taken part in the actual management of patients and felt the difficulties and had great understanding of them. Samuel is known to us mainly from his writings, in which he appears as a humble-minded man; this is especially true of his *Memoirs*. But he struck others as a powerful personality. He may easily have dominated Allis, and he would do so very acceptably. It must have been the case that without any appointment or mention in the Minutes, or in his *Memoirs*, he did, in fact, train Jepson's successor.

Another culture-carrier was Hannah Ponsonby. Having come to The Retreat in 1797 to help look after her mother, who was a patient, Hannah had later been taken on to the staff, and she worked for many years under Katherine Jepson, who trained her in the ways of the place. She succeeded Katherine in 1823, when the Jepsons retired. The few stories that survive about her suggest that, like Katherine, she had the gift of managing and making things pleasant. The women who came out from York on Mondays to help mend sheets found these occasions jolly. Her influence must have been great and she was certainly popular. Elizabeth Pumphrey, Allis' daughter, said 'she had several pronounced lovers in the house'.

And of course some of the patients were, in their own ways, culture-carriers. Many of them stayed a long time at The Retreat, and would know exactly what had to be done and when. The fundamental basis of the community life at The Retreat lay in the confidence and co-operation which Jepson patently won from each individual, by understanding and active kindness according to each one's need, a most time-consuming method. This kind of relationship depends upon insight and is much less easily transmitted than organisation.

Allis did not take long to develop this insight. Those of his friends who had told him that he would be equal to the job guessed right. He remained at The Retreat for seventeen years and 'became fond of the employment'.

That The Retreat went on its tranquil way, undamaged by the departure of the Jepsons, the death of William Tuke and the arrival of Thomas Allis, is made clear by the reports of visitors from outside the Quaker group, who supported The Retreat. Dr. Ferrus, at one time physician to Napoleon I, came in 1826, four years after William Tuke's death. He was well aware of Tuke's principles. He described him as 'a man in whose eyes neither riches nor poverty, imbecility nor genius, ought in the slightest degree to affect the bonds that hold all men in common. He thought, with reason, that justice and force ought to be evinced not by shouts and menaces, but by gentleness of character and calm of mind'. He continued: 'The traditions of this friend of humanity are preserved in the house which he founded. Everything, even down to the patients, is silent and peaceful in this asylum, where some who are not members of the Society of Friends are also admitted. Those admitted, whatever their religion or social conditions may have been, influenced by the tranquillity of the place and the force of example, find repose in this house, which much more resembles a convent of Trappists than a madhouse'. It was actually in the same year that Dr. Conolly visited The Retreat and was 'deeply impressed'.

About the same time, the Italian, Count Pecchio, visited The Retreat. He described the pleasantness of the situation, the openness, 'no window bars, no iron gates, no guards', and the quiet within. 'I heard no howling, no lamentations; all was in the utmost neatness, no bad smell . . . Out of eighty patients, male and female, there was not one in a state of coercion . . . When I entered the sitting room, some were playing, some reading, some writing. In the women's rooms some of the inmates were at work, and a person coming in, without being apprised beforehand, would have believed himself at first among persons of sound mind, so great is the decorum and tranquillity which the matron (Hannah Ponsonby) knows so well how to preserve.'

And finally it is significant that an article in *The Sketch*, published for The Retreat Committee in 1828, was somewhat critical of the early months of its history, when it was managed by William Tuke, who was quite inexperienced, and Cardingley, who had probably had the wrong kind of experience: but *The Sketch* had no criticism to make of the regime of Allis.

So we can conclude that the noble tradition of the founders did not die with them, but was bequeathed undiminished, to their successors. An American physician from New York, who visited asylums in

England in 1863, wrote: 'The York Retreat . . . hallowed in the memory of everyone who appreciates the spirit of benevolence which originated it and has ever since pervaded its halls still pursues its mission . . . It was sufficiently apparent that the genius and earnestness of Tuke still abides among his successors'.

Editor's Footnote

This story of the founding of The Retreat is one example among the many in British history of how vital reforms, affecting the welfare of incalculable numbers of people, have been set in motion by the initiative and enterprise of private individuals, who have given their services with no ambition for financial enrichment. The Tukes were people of substance and so in his way was George Jepson, but they were unqualified in the technical sense for the work they chose to do, and many of their colleagues were hardly educated in the conventional sense at all. This was the case with large numbers of social reformers. The indebtedness of our own generation to unqualified and socially unrecognised men and women who did such frontier work in the 19th and early 20th century, usually managing on the thinnest of financial margins, should never be forgotten.

Since World War I, our political leaders have contrived with mixed results to re-organise and nationalise all sorts of movements which began as The Retreat had done. Humane legislation, access to public funds, insistence on paper qualifications, together with well publicised career structures, have done much to further these causes, but such measures do not in themselves make for a truly 'Welfare State'. We still need the devotion, persistence and personal concern for the miserable which characterised people like the Tukes and the Jepsons.

As this book goes to press, The Retreat, now a registered Nursing Home, is still administered as a Charity by the members of the Society of Friends. It is still surrounded by forty acres of beautiful grounds on Lamel Hill, the highest point in the city of York. There is accommodation for 230 patients, either in single rooms or small dormitories. In administrative organisation and in medical techniques there have been massive changes, naturally enough, but the heart of the place remains where Old William, as his family affectionately dubbed him, meant it to be.

Appendix A

D. H. Tuke in his **History of the Insane in the British Isles,** Appendix C, gives the following list of asylums in operation in 1792:

Bethlem Hospital. Used for lunatics about 1400 A.D.

St. Luke's Hospital. Founded 1751.

Liverpool Royal Lunatic Hospital, associated with the Royal Infirmary. 1792.

Manchester Royal Lunatic Hospital, in connection with the Royal Infirmary. 1706. (Removed to Cheadle 1849.)

Bethel Hospital, Norwich. 1713.

The Lunatic Ward of Guy's Hospital. 1728. (New building 1797.)

The York Lunatic Hospital, Bootham. 1777.

St. Peter's Hospital, Bristol. Incorporated 1696.

Brooke House, Clapton (Dr. Munro's). 1759.

Hoxton Asylum. 1744.

Fonthill-Gifford, Hindon, Wilts. 1718.

Droitwich Asylum. 1791.

Belle Grove House, Newcastle-on-Tyne. 1766.

Lea Pale House, Stoke, near Guildford. 1744.

Appendix B

The laws for the control of the poor affected the insane.

i) Vagrancy Laws. Time out of mind vagrants were dreaded. 'Hark, hark, the dogs do bark, the beggars are coming to town.' Sturdy beggars, especially in groups, and especially if they were hungry, could be dangerous; they would attack travellers, and shops and markets were not safe from them. The dogs were right to bark. Traditionally men wandering 'with no visible means of subsistence' were supposed to be whipped, fed and taken back to their own parish in a cart; their own parish was responsible for them. But this was expensive and gave rise to much litigation, as one parish tried to shift the obligation to another. In 1555 a new plan was tried. In Brideswell, near Blackfriars, a building was set aside where vagrants were to be housed and fed and made to work. This idea spread and gradually there came to be a number of Brideswells over the country; they were used also for confining insane people found wandering.

(ii) Laws concerning poverty. Poverty was always a problem but from time to time there were crises, when enclosures of land, or changes in the value of money, or other causes greatly increased destitution. Monasteries and parish churches undertook some relief of the poor; monasteries had traditionally given aid to the sick and hospitality to strangers, and each parish raised a poor rate for the relief of unemployment and other destitution. This principle was re-affirmed and revised by the Elizabethan Poor Law of 1601, which remained in force until 1834.

But the burden of the Poor Rate on rate-payers seemed continually to grow more intolerable. In 1722 a departure was made from this Elizabethan Law that relief could be given to people by small money grants in their own homes, and a new law was passed. This was intended to reduce the number making claims on the poor rate. By this law rate-payers were empowered to build workhouses. Those receiving relief were to come into the workhouse, where the able-bodied were to be made to work and those who could not work were to be housed and fed, and residence at the workhouse was to be a condition of relief. They were not meant to be happy places; the intent was that conditions were to be so distasteful that people would do anything rather than go and live in them. This idea was very successful from the point of view of those responsible for finance. During the 19th century *The Times* used to record cases of persons found dead in the streets from starvation. Enquiry seemed always to establish that they had not died from mere starvation, but from pneumonia. It appears that some people would rather walk about the street with pneumonia, and starving, until they dropped, than go to the Guardians of the Poor.

Workhouses came to be used for the confinement of insane persons. No special rooms were set aside for them and their presence inexpressibly increased the wretchedness of the other inmates; widows, old people, young unmarried mothers and others, many of them people who all their lives until now had been respectable, were tormented by the teasing, noise, insolence and disgusting habits of the insane and the imbecile, and also by the way in which the attendants dealt with them.

Appendix C

The case of Mary Lamb illustrates the lenity of the law when the insanity was held to be proven. She was an obedient, compliant, serviceable daughter until the day when she suddenly went out of her mind and stabbed her mother to death with the breadknife. Her brother Charles came into the room just in time to wrest the knife from her and save his father's life. Mary was never accused of murder. In the coroner's court the coroner accepted the plea that she had been insane at the time, though the insane fit had passed off. At his request Mary was put into the care of her brother, and Charles devoted the rest of his life to her. He had already given up all idea of marriage, and the Quaker girl called Hester, in whom he was interested, probably never knew of his feeling.

Another case of clemency on the ground of insanity was that of Margaret Nicholson, who made an attempt on the life of King George III, and was not executed. This was in 1786, two years before the King himself became ill. She approached him as he was getting out of his carriage, as if to present a petition, and jabbed at his breast with an old and bent dessert knife. 'A yeoman of the guard caught her arm and wrested the weapon from her, exclaiming "She has a knife. Is your Majesty hurt?" The King instantly replied, stroking his hand on his waistcoat, "No, I am not hurt - take care of the woman - do not hurt her for she is mad" '. After an endless amount of enquiry she was legally declared insane and sent to Bethlem, where she lived for some forty years. In this case the trouble that was taken to establish insanity is probably to be accounted for by the attitude of the King.

The definition of insanity lay with the judges, who made very narrow conditions. In her book *Lunacy, Law & Conscience*, Professor Kathleen Jones quotes from R. V. Arnold, 1723, a case of attempted murder. Justice Tracey said: 'It is not every kind of frantic humour, or something unaccountable in a man's behaviour, that points him out to be such a man as is exempt from punishment; it must be a man that is totally deprived of his understanding and memory, and doth not know what he is doing, no more than an infant, than a brute or wild beast; such a one is never the object of punishment'. Dr. Jones concludes that 'the vast majority of those who would now be considered criminally insane . . . were punished as ordinary criminals.

Appendix D

The Hippocratic Oath

See *Encyclopaedia Britannica* under Medicine and Surgery, History of. Also Chadwick and Mann, *Medical Works of Hippocrates New Translation* 1950 page 9.

I swear by Apollo the healer, by Aesculapius, by Health and all the powers of healing, and call to witness all the gods and goddesses, that I will keep this oath and promise to the best of my ability and judgment. I will pay the same respect to my master in the science as to my parents and share my life with him and pay all my debts to him. I will regard his sons as my brothers and teach them the science if they desire to learn it without fee or contract. I will hand on precepts, lectures and all other learning to my sons and those of my master and to those pupils duly sworn and apprenticed, and to none other.

I will use my power to help the sick to the best of my ability and judgment; and I will abstain from wronging or harming any man by it. I will not give a fatal draught to anyone if I am asked; nor will I suggest any such thing. Neither will I give a woman the means to procure an abortion. I will be chaste and religious in my life and in my practice. I will not cut even for the stone, but I will leave such procedures to the practitioners of that craft. Whenever I go into a house, I will go to help the sick and never with the intention of doing harm or injury. I will not abuse my position to indulge in sexual contacts with the bodies of men or women, whether they be slave or free. Whatever I see or hear, professionally or privately, which ought not to be divulged I will keep secret and tell no one. If therefore I observe this oath and do not violate it, may I prosper in my life and in my profession, earning good repute among all men for all time. If I transgress and forswear this oath, may my lot be otherwise.

Appendix E

George III's Illness

King George's illness had important effects upon the general attitude to madness, and his treatment illustrates common practice. George III was widely beloved; Fanny Burney's *Letters* reveal the strong affection for 'the dear and good King' in court circles; he was also a popular figure in the country at large. In 1788 he had an obscure illness, now called porphyria. The word porphyria means the dark purple colour which appears in the urine when this illness is fully developed; this symptom was not noted by the King's doctors, who would be unaware of its significance. Porphyria in its acute form gives rise to delirium, which can easily be mistaken for madness. But there was no way then of diagnosing the congenital fault in the chemical metabolism of the nerves, which produces the delirium. The court physicians who were responsible for him were completely baffled, and though the opinion was occasionally voiced that his condition was delirium and not madness (i.e. a physical disorder, not a disorder of the mind) he had to be treated as mad. But his doctors had no experience of treating madness and were quite at a loss; everyone at Court perceived this.

When at last it became common property that the King's illness was madness, the general horror and contempt of insanity turned to universal sympathy. The King's illness was horrible; he had a variety of symptoms - extreme agitation, talkativeness (of which he was sometimes uncomfortably aware, he did not wish to cause distress), hoarseness, colic, high pulse rate, insomnia, loss of appetite so that he became very thin, and for part of the time, fever with copious sweating. The most distressing feature of the illness itself, for him and for those who loved him, was the climactic confusion of mind. But his sufferings were added to by treatment. His doctors prevented him for weeks from seeing the Queen or his daughters. The poulticing of his ankles, on which they insisted, caused ulceration and much pain.

His distresses were increased when Dr. Willis arrived. He was a clergyman who ran an asylum for thirty patients in Lincolnshire. He was not a Member of the Royal College of Physicians, and not socially on a level with the physicians already in charge of the King. He was brought in on the appeal of one of the ladies of the court, Lady Harcourt, who said Dr. Willis had greatly helped her mother-in-law in a similar illness. He was the only doctor in attendance on the King who had any experience of handling the insane. Because he had that experience, as well as on the ground of his humble social standing, he was disliked and despised by the Royal physicians; they intended him to be the keeper to the King, that is in constant attendance on him, under their orders. But Dr. Willis had no such intention; he was accustomed to exercising complete and unchallenged control over his patients, and his understanding of his business at court was that the King was to be his patient, whom he would treat as he always did treat patients.

Willis won the confidence of the Queen, because he took responsibility in the sick room. Before he came no one had exercised responsibility. He quickly won the confidence of the Ministers of the Government, for of course the illness of the King was a political earthquake. It was realised that if his madness went on for long, especially if, as was feared, it became a chronic condition, there would have to be a regency. The Prince of Wales wanted to be Regent. The Ministers knew the Prince to be a very different character from his father, and sure to change as much as possible as soon as he assumed regency powers. They were therefore very anxious to find a doctor who would say that the King would recover in a short time. The only one of the seven doctors who would say this, and he said it again and again, was Dr. Willis. He believed that nine out of ten of his patients always did recover. (Under interrogation he wavered and admitted that he had not kept notes of cases, and could not prove anything about the rate of recovery of those under his care.)

Members of the Government several times questioned the group of doctors very closely about the prognosis for the King. All but Dr. Willis hedged. During one of these interrogations, Willis was criticised for his rashness in allowing his patient to get his hand upon a razor; the consequences if the King had managed to cut his throat would have been appalling. Dr. Willis explained that the King had not been shaved for a long time, and that the man who did eventually do him this service had not shaved his upper lip. Willis was sitting by the King and 'Being confident from his Professions and the Humour of His Majesty at that moment, I suffered His Majesty to shave His Lips Himself . . . It is necessary for the Physician, especially in such cases, to be able to judge at the Moment, whether he can confide in the Profession of his patient. I was never disappointed in my opinion'. Willis also allowed the King to pare his nails with a knife, as they needed cutting very badly.

It makes a lot of difference to the morale of men whether they are decently shaved or not. The same is often true of the appearance of the nails. The fact that the King was not properly shaved or manicured is evidence that the royal doctors were not really regarding their patient as a man with ordinary feelings.

Willis achieved a dominant position and eventually succeeded in excluding the physicians from the sick room and managing the King without reference to them.

His treatment was severe; it included continual dosing with tartarized antimony, which is an emetic. The King was always being sick, but did not know why, because the emetic was disguised in the food he was given. It does not seem surprising that he lost his appetite. But the most unpleasant part of Willis' treatment was the means he took to achieve an ascendancy over the King. This was in effect the straitwaistcoat. 'For every non-compliance – refusing food when he had difficulty in swallowing, no appetite or a return of colic, resisting going to bed when he was too agitated and restless to lie down, throwing off his bedclothes during sweating attacks – he was clamped into the straitwaistcoat, often with a band across his chest and his legs tied to the bed.' The King of course intensely disliked Dr. Willis. Many months later 'he talked of the coercion used and asked how a man could sleep with his arms pinioned in a straitwaistcoat and his legs tied to the bedposts?' When his physical strength began to improve, additional confinement was used by day. The comment of Macalpine and Hunter on this treatment is 'a great deal of the trouble and violence that ensued was in direct response to the control and coercion to which he was subjected and against which he rebelled. Unfortunately the lesson that harsh treatment makes violent patients, and that violence is often a reaction of fear, was not learned until the nineteenth century'.

But the King's natural strength triumphed over his illness and his treatments and he recovered. His illness later and finally did become chronic. But he had twelve years of health after the 1788 attack. The public respected him greatly for the courage with which he took up his duties as soon as he was able, and this confirmed their altered feeling about mental illness, which had been excited by Dr. Willis' insistence that 'insanity is curable'.

Note: This account of the King's illness is indebted throughout to Macalpine & Hunter, *George III and the Mad Business.*

Appendix F

George Perceval (son of the Lord Perceval who was Prime Minister and was assassinated in 1812) became deranged in 1834, and his mother and brother arranged for him to go to Brislington, to the institution run by Dr. Fox. He thought that in making this choice they were influenced by the beauty of the scenery. This patient four years later wrote about his experiences there.

Perceval was not sure at the time that he was mad. He constantly heard voices, which claimed to be supernatural, commanding him to do outrageous, violent, indecent things, and threatening him with awful supernatural penalties if he did not comply. (This is a typical schizophrenic symptom.) He did not know whether the voices were hallucinations or not. He knew that he was behaving badly, he was too scared to disobey them, in case they really were supernatural and in case the fearful punishments they threatened were really lying in wait for him. He probably believed in hell before he went out of his mind. He thought he really was sane at bottom, because he did realise that it was open to question whether the voices were hallucinatory or not. They plagued him a great deal and he thought it was very unkind that nobody would discuss his condition with him and help him to see the truth. Gradually by close attention he began to perceive that some of the things the voices foretold did not happen, and he freed himself from their dominance. This was the beginning of his recovery, which apparently took two or three years.

The first result of his being at the asylum seemed to be that he got much worse. A matter which angered him very much was that his *amour propre* was continually affronted; he did not get the deference which he felt was owing to a nobleman. He objected to the manners of his keepers. They did not hit him or use physical force upon him, though he says that he sometimes hit out at them; but they were jocular and familiar. When he was obliged by way of treatment, to be ducked in a cold bath, he felt he should not have had to get into water that had been used by other men, indeed he should have had privacy for the whole performance. When at length he nerved himself to complain to Dr. Fox, the reply he got was 'But has not Jesus made us all equal?' It was clear to him that the man was a 'sectarian' and was letting 'the burlesque notions of his sect seep into his treatment'. He thought it was intolerable of his mother and brother to have consigned him, in his trouble 'in spite of my intellectual powers', to a sectarian. He was subjected to chains and straps in a niche in the common room by day, and to straps at night, and although he knew that he could be dangerously violent, he reacted bitterly against such treatment. Some of Perceval's recollections of this traumatic period are very significant. 'I needed quiet, I needed tranquillity, I needed security. I needed at times even seclusion. I could not obtain them.' 'My will, my wishes, my repugnancies, my habits, my delicacy, my inclinations, my necessities were never once consulted.' 'Then I hated, I despised, I was enraged, I became hardened, I . . . was brutalised.' 'I will be bound to say that the greatest part of the violence that occurs in lunatic asylums is to be attributed to the conduct of those who are dealing with the disease, not the disease itself.' 'Because I did not respect myself, they disrespected me, whereas they should have brought me to my senses by greater reserve and respect.'

In the end his family took him away; he went to another asylum and recovered enough to be discharged – and to marry – how the marriage fared we do not know.

It is not fair to judge an asylum on the criticism of a patient. But it is worth attending to this book with some care, in spite of the fact that Perceval was a nobleman and the doctor a Quaker, so that a high degree of objectivity on the patient's part is not to be expected. It is a very moving book; the man is telling us what it is like to be mad. I know of no book by a patient at The Retreat that gives us such a vivid and painful account of the experience of mental illness. (*Perceval's Narrative*, ed. Gregory Bateson, Stamford University Press 1961.)

A Selected Book List

Black, *Comparative View of the Mortality of the Human Species of all ages and of the Diseases and Casualties by which they are destroyed or annoyed.* 1788

Brayshaw, A. Neave, *The Quakers, their Story and their Message:* Sessions 1982

Conolly, Dr. John, *On the Treatment of the Insane without mechanical Restraint:* London 1856

Cullen, W. M.D., *First Lines of the Practice of Physic:* Edinburgh 1784

Ferriar, J., *Medical Histories and Reflections:* Warrington 1792

Gray, Jonathan, *A History of the York Lunatic Asylum:* York 1815

Haslam, J., *Observations on Madness and Melancholy:* London 1809

Hill, R. Gardiner, *The Non Restraint System of Treatment in Lunacy:* Simpkin Marshall, London 1857

Hunt, H.C., *A Retired Habitation.* A history of The Retreat at York: H.K. Lewis, London 1932

Jacobi, Dr., *On the Construction and Management of Hospitals for the Insane:* 1841

Jones, Kathleen, Ph.D., *Lunacy Law and Conscience 1744-1845:* Routledge & Kegan Paul 1955

Jones, Kathleen, Ph.D., *Mental Health & Social Policy 1845-59:* Routledge & Kegan Paul 1960

Jones, Kathleen, Ph.D., *Mental Hospitals at Work:* Routledge & Kegan Paul 1962

Macalpine, Ida & R. Hunter, *George III and the Mad Business:* London 1969

Mennell, Robert, *Tea:* An historical Sketch

Parry Jones, Dr. W. L., *The Trade in Lunacy:* A Study of Madhouses in England in the 18th and 19th centuries: London 1972

Paternoster, B., *The Madhouse System,* published by the Author in 1841

Rush, Benjamin, Physician, *Medical Enquiries and Observations upon the Diseases of the Mind:* Philadelphia 1812

Select Committees of the House of Commons, 1815-1816 reports

Sessions, William K. & E. Margaret, *The Tukes of York:* Sessions 1971

Smith, the Rev. Sydney, *Description of The Retreat* in *The Edinburgh Review:* 1814

Stark, William, *Remarks on the Construction and Management of Lunatic Asylums*

Suttie, Ian, *Origins of Love and Hate:* London 1935

Tuke, Daniel Hack, *Chapters in the History of the Insane in the British Isles:* Kegan Paul 1882

Tuke, Daniel Hack, *Reform in the Treatment of the Insane:* 1892

Tuke, Samuel, *Description of The Retreat:* York 1813

Tuke, Samuel, *Notes on the Design of Asylums:* 1812

Tuke, Samuel, *Practical Hints on the Construction & Economy of Pauper Lunatic Asylums:* 1815

Tuke, Samuel, *Review of the Early History of The Retreat:* 1846

Wesley, John, *Primitive Physic; an Easy and Natural Way of Curing Most Diseases:* London 1870

York Monthly Meeting Records: 1823

Index

GALEN, Greek physician, 2nd century A.D., 7-8
Gartnavel Hospital, Glasgow, 73
George III and his illness, 1, 96, 98-100
Grand Dukes Nicholas and Michael of Russia, visited The Retreat, 73
Gray, Jonathan, author of *An Account of York Asylum*, 75
Gurney, Elizabeth (Mrs. Fry), 20, 49, 64, 73
Gurney family, 13

HALL, Hannah, member of the domestic staff at The Retreat, 36, 43
Hanwell Hospital, 4-5, 36, 62, 77-9
Harvey family, 13
Haslam, Dr. John, apothecary at Bethlem Hospital, 1795-1816, 3, 6-7, 64
Higgins, Godfrey, magistrate in York, 74
Hippocrates of Cos, 7-8, 97
Hipsley, John, junior, married Mabel Tuke, 25, 31
John, senior, 35, 38, 46
Hodge, Mrs., death under forcible feeding, 64
Holt, Mrs. Mary, patient at The Retreat, 36
Hospital Bonifacio, Florence, 53
Hoyland, Elizabeth, first wife of William Tuke, 17, 23-4, 26

JEPSON, George, Superintendent at The Retreat, 1797 till 1823, 26, 35, 46-7, 67, et seq., 73, 80, 87, 89-90, 92
his innovations, 54-5
his management of patients, 56-8, 63
marriage to Katherine Allen, 59
his management of violent patients, 61-2, 88
his attitude to forcible feeding, 64
Sydney Smith's admiration for him, 73
his old age, 81-2
his retirement, 83
his death, 1836, 84
Katherine, née Allen, see Allen, Katherine
Johnson, Dr. Samuel, 24
Jones, Dr. Kathleen, historian of the treatment of mental illness, vi, 60, 96

KING, Jane, housekeeper at The Retreat, 35-6, 41-2, 81
Kitching, Thomas, member of The Retreat committee, 88
Knaresborough, 46-7, 55

LAMB, Charles and Mary, 2, 6, 34-5, 96
Letter on Pauper Asylums, 1815, by Samuel Tuke, 58
Lloyd, Charles, poet and patient at The Retreat, 71

MACALPINE & Hunter, authors of *George III and the Mad Business*, 69, 100
Mad houses, 2-3, 6
Marcus Aurelius, Roman Emperor, 161-180 A.D., 7-8
Maud, Esther, second wife of William Tuke, see Tuke, Esther
Timothy, William Tuke's brother-in-law, 8, 26, 35, 38
William, 8, 46
Mills, Hannah, patient at York Asylum, died 1791, xii, 25-6, 29
Monro, Dr., Physician at Bethlem Hospital, 8
The Mount School, York 22, 27
Murray, Lindley, grammarian, 22, 29-30, 50

NICHOLSON, Margaret, attempted attack on George III, 96

OUSE Bridge, 23
Owen, Robert, cotton manufacturer, 73

PAISLEY shawls, 20
Parry Jones, Dr. W. Ll., author, 6, 41
Pecchio, Count, visited The Retreat, 90
Perceval, George, mental patient at Brislington, 101-2
Physical Restraint, use of in treating the mentally ill, 5-6, 8, 62-3, 76, 78
Pinel, Philippe, Physician at the Bicêtre Hospital, Paris, 53
Ponsonby, Hannah, nurse and later matron at The Retreat, 34, 89-90
Poor Laws, 1, 94-5
Priestman, Thomas, member of The Retreat Committee, 34
Pumphrey, Elizabeth, née Allis, see Allis, Elizabeth
William, 86

RETTON, Ann, in charge of women patients at The Retreat, 36, 39, 57
Rogers, John, apothecary, evidence given to the Select Committee 1815-6, 63
Row, Mrs. Rachel, patient at The Retreat, 37
Rowntree family, 13